D1283062

FLYING TALES FROM 'BLACKWOOD'

Series II

FLYING TALES

FROM

'BLACKWOOD'

Series II

WILLIAM BLACKWOOD & SONS LIMITED

EDINBURGH AND LONDON

1967

PRINTED IN GREAT BRITAIN BY
WILLIAM BLACKWOOD & SONS LTD., EDINBURGH

SBN 85158 000 9

FLYING TALES

FROM

' BLACKWOOD '

Series II

WILLIAM BLACKWOOD & SONS LIMITED

EDINBURGH AND LONDON

1967

PRINTED IN GREAT BRITAIN BY
WILLIAM BLACKWOOD & SONS LTD., EDINBURGH

SBN 85158 000 9

CONTENTS

1 **A Chapter of Accidents**   1
    Air Vice-Marshal T. C. Traill, C.B., O.B.E., D.F.C.

2 **Different Techniques**   15
    A. G. D.

3 **Sun Tan 27**   29
    Nosmo

4 **Sunday Dawn, Sunday Dusk**   40
    D. E. Charlwood

5 **Totem Flight 347**   59
    Jonathan Spence

6 **A Glimpse of the Stratosphere**   82
    Tony Smythe

7 **How Goes It ?**   92
    M. D. L.

8 **Skydiving**   119
    John Allen

Continued overleaf

9 **The Breath of Life**   134
    Group Captain A. G. Dudgeon, C.B.E., D.F.C.

10 **The Cumulo-Nimbus Cloud**   146
    James Thomson

11 **' Leads the Field '**   155
    Wing Commander K. P. Smales, D.S.O., D.F.C.

12 **The Air Race**   185
    Brian Haimes

13 **Re-Borne with Wings**   204
    John Brooks

14 **The Long Way Back**   220
    D. E. Charlwood

15 **Aquiline Activity**   241
    James Montgomery Robinson

16 **Snow on My Tail**   270
    Daphne Pochin Mould

Biographical Notes on the Authors   286

1

A CHAPTER OF ACCIDENTS

Air Vice-Marshal T. C. Traill, C.B., O.B.E., D.F.C.

This is a catalogue of most of the accidents and some of the incidents [1] which happened to me between learning to fly in 1917 and retiring in 1954. I was prompted to write it in hospital, after what I hope was my last crash, when several of my visitors asked me if it was my first.

Most of the accidents occurred in the early days as a result of enemy action or lack of training. It is difficult for a pilot trained by a qualified flying instructor to appreciate the extent of our ignorance. To make it more difficult there was no means of communication except by shutting off the engine and shouting, and I have a clear recollection of the sergeant who taught me jerking back the throttle, clouting me over my helmet and yelling:

" What the bloody hell do you think you are doing, sir?"

My first crash was at Netheravon in 1917, and I do not remember anything about it except waking in a hospital near Stonehenge and finding my mother and sister, who had travelled by train from a village in Essex, by my bed.

[1] An 'incident' in the language of the Accidents Prevention Branch is something, *e.g.*, a mechanical failure or a human error, which might have led to an accident but did not.

It had happened on my third solo in a Maurice Farman, a pusher in which the pilot sat out in front of everything in a shallow nacelle with pedals and handlebars. I had become inverted at about 800 feet and, after staying that way for a while, had glided in till my head and the top plane hit the ground together. I never knew what happened—whether the cause was mechanical failure or stupidity: of one thing I am sure, I was not trying to do anything exciting or clever.

After hospital and completing training I joined a Bristol Fighter squadron in France. They were fine aeroplanes, two-seater fighters and very strong. The pilot had a fixed forward-firing gun and the observer one or two Lewis-guns on a ' Scarff ring ' mounting immediately behind the pilot. The observer stood inside the ring, which was on a level with his lower ribs: there was also a small seat for him facing aft, but he never used it over the lines.

When I arrived in the Squadron, Lieutenant Jones, an experienced observer, was free, and he and I flew together till he was killed. I never knew his Christian name or where he came from, or if he had a family or any other interest except to engage the enemy more closely ; but the side of him that I knew, I trusted absolutely.

Our first bit of trouble was caused by over-enthusiasm: going down to ' mix it ' with some Fokker triplanes and getting separated from our formation. When I tried to disengage, three or four of them got under my tail and shot us up badly. Jones, returning fire, did not allow for his gunsights being six inches above the barrel of his gun and shot away several inches of one of my main fuselage members where it was, or had been, joined by two struts and four bracing-wires. At the same time the Fokkers had shot holes in the other three longerons, so that when I was forced to turn again and dive on them I was aware of a sinuous motion and, looking up and backwards over my shoulder, I saw the tail undulating horribly behind us.

After a very short burst with the front gun I pulled carefully out of the dive and turned gently for home. We were cold meat, but for some reason the enemy let us go. One Tripe did come up on the starboard side, not shooting at us, but Jones, though his gun-mounting was shot up and jammed, managed to reach round and fire a short burst in his general direction and he threw a roll and went home.

Even without the enemy it was an anxious flight home, with the tail assembly following us more as if it were on tow than a vital part of us. Jones and I had formed the habit, without anything said on either side, of shaking hands when we crossed the lines on the way home after a fight. As I reached over my shoulder this time I said I was worried about the tail, and I can still hear his completely confident reply as he leaned over me in the slipstream:

" That's all right: I've got my eye on it."

When almost within gliding distance of our aerodrome, a grass field near St Omer, we ran out of fuel, because one of the tanks had a bullet-hole in it. I then found that the tail trimming-gear had been hit and jammed in the forward position, and that only half of my elevator was working. The result of all this was that with the stick right back we glided at between 80 and 85 m.p.h. I was afraid that the tail would fall off if I put the nose down to get speed to help me to flatten out, so I just let her go on in.

Jones had a forced-landing technique of his own. Just

3

before we touched down, he used to fix his gun over the side so that it could not swing round and hit him. Then he would sit facing aft, fold his arms and relax. I think his plan was based on the theory that a drunk man falls easily: certainly this time, as we broke in half and folded up, he was thrown well forward, and neither of us had more than a cut or two and a bruise. We picked ourselves up and walked in, amused and laughing with relief from tension.

In the next three weeks Jones and I had three forced landings on our side of the lines as a result of action with the enemy on the other side. On the first I hit and killed a cow, which stood us on our nose. A peasant woman and her daughter arrived before we had climbed out of the aircraft and started to upbraid us. They were not allowed to get far, for Jones had had a trying time. He had finished his ammunition some time before the end of the flight ; then my gun had refused to fire more than single shots and we had had to spin almost into the ground to get away from three persistent Fokker biplanes. Jones had had no way of knowing whether I was spinning to get away or because we were out of control: now he lost his temper. And the British paid for the cow.

The second landing was of little interest, but the third was unusual. As we were coming back to the lines near Ypres under A.A. fire, something fairly large entered the front tank through the bottom centre section and loosed a stream of pressured petrol at my stomach. I was soaked in the stuff from the navel down, and undid my belt in case the machine caught fire ; I had no parachute, but felt that a free fall was preferable to burning, though if she had caught fire I would have been alight too before I could get out. We crossed the lines near Ypres, and

4

there being no place where we could possibly make a landing I glided straight on waiting for the crash while Jones went through his procedure. But there was no crash: some noise, a powerful deceleration, and there we were on the ground, in one piece, wrapped and festooned in the spider's-web wiring of a Signal Corps Headquarters.

After the unpleasantness of bracing oneself or in Jones's case relaxing for a crash, it was pleasant to be on the ground without one. The Signal Corps people were very decent about it too.

The next affair was Jones's last. We were flying in loose formation, making a running fight for the lines with a strong west wind in our faces and a cloud of Fokker biplanes behind and among us. I had just shot one off a Bristol's tail when we allowed our attention to concentrate for a few seconds on another Bristol that was spinning slowly down in flames past our starboard wing. In those few seconds we were bounced by another Fokker from very close astern. Jones gave our 'extreme emergency' signal, a tap on top of my head, in time for me to take violent evasive action as the Fokker opened fire. He only fired the shortest of bursts but Jones was hit, the aileron controls were shot away and the undercarriage was shot through. Then we were alone again: possibly another Bristol had made a pass at him.

The aircraft, though defenceless, was stable enough without ailerons to fly back across the lines. Jones was on his seat with his head resting against his gun-mounting: he looked peaceful and relaxed and was quite still. When I put my hand on his shoulder I knew he was dead.

After a few flights with an observer who was killed on

a sortie with another pilot, I was joined by Lieutenant Gordon-Bennett. We flew together for two months till he was wounded in a dog-fight. I was turning on a Fokker's tail: I knew another was shooting at me, but he was so far away that I thought it safe enough to disregard him. But I was wrong: there was a 'clickety-click' as we flew through his line of fire, and a great shout from behind: "I'm hit!" I disengaged in a long, steep spiral dive (I expect the Fokker pilot claimed me as 'destroyed') and made for home, where we found that G.-B. had a painful wound in the leg from which, I am glad to say, he made a complete recovery.

After Gordon-Bennett I was joined by Captain Burbage, and a few days later we were gliding across the lines with an empty front tank and a fair-sized hole in the top of the rear one. This released the air pressure needed to feed the petrol to the engine, which petered out. We landed on a flat patch where the cavalry had been exercising their horses, and were made welcome by the officers. They apologised for being unable to offer us breakfast as they were about to move up, but they gave us instead two bowls each of whisky and water. The whisky on an empty stomach—it was 7 A.M.—was effective. I plugged the hole in the tank with clay: Burbage held the stuff in position while I pumped up the air pressure, then three troopers who had never touched an aeroplane before pulled the propeller round and we flew home as whistled as coots.

Burbage and I were together for nearly a month. Then one still autumn evening, drifting home at 8000 feet in wide open formation on our side of the lines, a man who should not have been there flew into me from behind. His starboard wing hit my port wing and folded right back: with lift only on his port side he rolled rapidly towards us and his undamaged wing nearly hit us again as he fell into a fast spin in which he remained till he hit the ground. He was killed, but his observer recovered.

We were in trouble too. The outer rear inter-plane strut was broken ; one of the ailerons sailed off on its own ; four or five feet of both port wing-tips were damaged and crumpled, and despite full rudder and stick, the aircraft slipped into a steep left-hand spiral. I remember the feeling of regret and sadness as I looked down, and the touch of anger at having to go out in such an unnecessary way.

A few days before, realising that Burbage's knowledge of airmanship was pretty slight, I had asked him, if half the port wing was shot away, which wing he would get out on to bring the aircraft on to an even keel. After consideration, not realising that the undamaged wing would give more lift than the other, he had replied that he would get out on the port side because it would be lighter than the starboard. Now when I turned and called him to get out on the wing it was obvious that it was the starboard one that needed bringing down, but he remembered there was a catch in it and shouted, " Which wing?"

I told him and he started at once to climb past my cockpit and on to the bottom plane with his feet on the rear spar and holding on to the inter-plane bracing wires with his hands. He worked his way outwards until he came to the inner of the two inter-plane struts and then, to my intense surprise, for I had not believed it could happen, the aircraft came out of the spiral dive on to an even keel in a controllable glide. I called to him, " Right," and looked over the other side again to see what was happening to the other aircraft, but after a few moments our own machine took charge again and slipped away into the same steep spiral. On looking round I found Burbage on the side of my cockpit and about to climb back into his own ; he had taken it that when I called ' right ' he had done his part and was free to return to the comfort of the fuselage.

I shouted, " Get out again, you B.F.," and recognising the urgency he once more started to scramble out along the wing ; but we were getting critically low, and she only righted in time for me to begin to flatten out and get some of the speed off her before she hit the parados of an old trench with the bottom of the radiator and turned over hard.

I found myself pinned on my back with my legs in the air and petrol pouring on my face. (I tasted it for days afterwards.) With a struggle I was able to get clear, and after a few seconds in which to get my breath and my bearings I went to look for Burbage under his cockpit. Then a groan from the wing reminded me what had happened, and I found him with a badly damaged face lying by the strut to which he had been holding for his life. Two stretcher-bearers turned up, and later we had a long and terribly rough ride in the back of a Ford ambulance with Burbage sitting on my knee to cushion the bumps a little. It was a bad drive, but he made a complete recovery.

For years I felt that there was something phoney about this affair, because I knew that the weight of one man only half-way out along the wing could not have been enough to bring the aircraft under control. It was nearly twenty years later that it suddenly came to me that it was the drogue effect of Burbage on the wing, the drag of the wind on him and his big leather coat, that pulled us out of the turn and was the real cause of our survival.

Soon after the armistice I was lucky enough to be posted to the United States as Assistant Air Attaché and personal pilot to the Air Attaché, Air Commodore Charlton. In that period I had three forced landings.

The chance of engine failure was always uppermost in a pilot's mind in those days, and I therefore interject here a few words about forced landings in general. There is a certain minimum speed below which an aeroplane cannot get enough lift from the wings to support its weight: so when the engine fails and is no longer available to pull the machine through the air the pilot must put his machine into a downward glide, using the pull of gravity to replace the pull from the engine. Having selected the best field within gliding distance, the pilot must bring his aircraft down on such a path that he crosses the lee hedge with only a few feet of height to spare, and at a speed only a few miles an hour above stalling. If the lee hedge is crossed too high or too fast, the aircraft will, if the field is only just big enough, overshoot and hit the windward hedge, bank, wall or whatever the boundary may be.

If there is not quite enough height to clear the lee hedge or whatnot, the aircraft will hit it full pitch, at the stalling speed—much more dangerous than hitting the windward hedge after a bit of a run on the ground to get the speed off.

So when his engine fails, a pilot picks the most suitable field that he thinks is within his reach and then, by gliding in spirals, by ' S ' turns and by sideslipping, does his best to cross the lee boundary at the right height and speed. If he errs on the safe side he may break his aircraft against the windward boundary of a field quite big enough for a safe landing, and if he tries too hard to get his aircraft down in a small field he may hit the lee bank and kill himself.

The first of the American forced landings was in a Fokker D VI attached to a U.S. Army Air Force flying circus advertising the Victory Liberty Loan up and down the Middle West. The only interesting thing about it was that I was barely able to reach the race-track we were flying from. If I had been ten yards shorter I would have dropped her on the packed crowd of spectators lining the rails. I would then have been at fault for trying to land on the race-track instead of crashing her in another direction.

The next was in a Bristol Fighter which the Air Attaché had entered for a race from New York to San Francisco. We were piloting on alternate hops and had an engine failure on the second stage when I was in the back. The Air Commodore was out of practice and had no dual in the Bristol, and only one circuit with ballast in the back. He got her down well but rather fast in what seemed to us a good field until we found two strong wire fences across it. They turned us over, but not very hard, and the thing I remember best about the occasion was the friendship and hospitality of an old farmer and his family.

The third was when a Sopwith Snipe I had been sent, and knew almost nothing about, broke a connecting-rod over what seemed like the middle of New York. I was ferrying her to Washington at the time and was at 8000 feet, but even so there seemed to be no end to the built-up area. However, by gliding in the most hopeful-looking direction I reached a golf-course and made what would have been a good forced landing on a fairway if a gentleman playing a brassie shot had been prepared to move. To miss him I had to swing her into a shallow bunker where we stripped a tyre. I stayed the night with a garage mechanic and his family and had waffles and maple syrup for breakfast.

When I came home from the States the Service attitude to flying was changing. It had been rather happy-go-lucky. There were no maintenance forms to be checked before take-off, no system of pre-flight checks, and if you were going to fly a new type you might or might not get someone to tell you how to start the engine. One did some very stupid things and broke some aircraft unnecessarily, but now the approach to flying had become professional rather than amateur. Those of us who had survived had the chance to learn again, and I did not have another serious accident till 1932, in a Hawker Hart. We were flying in a ' V ' of nine in stratus cloud when we ran suddenly through a hundred-yard canyon of clear air into a heavy cumulus which was thick and turbulent. We all lost sight of each other immediately, and I started to do my break-up drill on my instruments. While doing this, my head in the cockpit, there was a crash and my aircraft went nose down out of control into a bunt, a downward loop.

The man who was flying in formation on me had held on for a moment before starting his own break-up drill, in the hope of seeing me again. Regrettably, he saw nothing until his propeller was cutting my fuselage in half within a few feet of Corporal Clemo, my air-gunner. It was a nasty moment for the Corporal, sitting facing aft, to see a propeller eating its way towards him. Clemo and I jumped while we were still bunting, and I had a bad fright, but a very short one, when I felt the stitching of my parachute-harness tearing as the canopy jerked open. It was meant to tear, but I thought it was failing and grabbed the shrouds for my life thinking my hand-hold was my only connection with the parachute, with 8000 feet still to go. I soon found my mistake, but then I heard another aircraft flying round us in the cloud with its engine running very badly. I told myself that it was long odds against its flying into a parachute, but it was comforting when it faded into the distance. I found later that it was the aircraft that had hit us and that the pilot was able to glide away and make a safe forced landing. Not knowing this at the time, I hoped when we emerged from the cloud to see three other parachutes, but there was only one, about fifty yards away. I called out, " Is that you, Clemo?" and he replied, bringing his heels together and giving a sort of salute, " O.K., sir."

People sometimes think that it must take a lot of nerve to jump out with a parachute, but as an alternative to sitting in an aeroplane that will not fly it is a delight ; and when you are floating down, still too high to worry about power-cables and suchlike, the view and the still-ness are lovely. As you get lower you begin to worry, if you are the worrying sort, about where you will land, and in the end the ground comes up disconcertingly quickly.

I landed through a birch-tree and my parachute stayed in the top of it, so that when I came to rest only the tips of my toes were on the ground and I had to release the harness to get the weight on my heels. Clemo landed unhurt in a field, but I had injured a knee when my para-chute opened: I had been travelling fast head downwards, and the damage occurred while I was being brought right way up with a jerk.

Finally, in 1953, a forced landing in a Firefly: a complete and sudden engine-failure which, I was relieved to find later, was not the result of mishandling on my part. I was about 3000 feet up and by the time I had looked round the cockpit and fiddled with the throttle and pitch-controls I was down to about 2000. I was not very worried ; I was sure to find a bit of grass or heath or plough long enough for a wheels-up landing, but the longer I looked the less I saw what I wanted, and as the ground approached I became very worried indeed. There is a moment when you realise that you have something to do which requires skill and judgment, and that if you fail you have had it. The fields were very small and surrounded by Cornish banks of rock and earth that were obviously lethal.

There was no wind, and I chose, or found myself committed, to try to land up a steep slope with only about 150 to 200 yards between the banks. It was not going to be enough, and as we crossed the lee bank I kicked on full left rudder and held off the bank. That was immediately effective: it felt as if the bottom had fallen out of her, so sudden was the stall, but we did not dig in or turn over so I cannot have dropped her far.

I found myself lying on my back looking up into a clear sky and beginning to work out where I was and why I was there. I was vaguely remembering that I had been going to crash a Firefly and that the bottom had fallen out of it, when I noticed that there was somebody with me (the local farmer who had pulled me out of the Firefly) and asked him, " Is there an aeroplane?"

" Yes," he replied, " just behind you: a Harvard."

That answer severed me again from the present: if I had just crashed a Harvard that affair with a Firefly may have been something that happened years before, it could

13

not have anything to do with my position here and now. Gradually, of course, I came fully round, and time and place came together again. (I have had trouble with time and space once or twice before—" Here I am ; I have had a fall, but that mud-walled village on the hillock is not here, it is fifty miles to the north.") The kind people from the farm looked after me and kept me warm until the ambulance arrived with a Medical Officer and morphia to help with the long drive to hospital.

Now I am retired and the aeroplanes we flew are museum pieces. I watch the handling of the Lightnings and Vulcans of today's Royal Air Force with gratitude and great respect, and I wish I could believe that I have put half as much into the Service as I have had out of it.

[' Maga ' March 1963.

2

DIFFERENT TECHNIQUES
A. G. D.

I

One day Steve rang me up. Steve is a Group Captain. "Would you like a balloon next Saturday?" Stalling for time and with visions of children's parties, I countered, " Perhaps ; why?" " Well," he continued, " I thought you might like to ride in one—or, maybe I should say, under one—and we could let it off from your place."

So it happened that on the Saturday morning there lay, stretched out on the grass, a large circle of rubberised material, made in alternate sectors of red and silver radiating from a gas-valve in the middle. Over the balloon was a large net, firmly pegged down at each corner. Beside it stood a large basket (just like Falstaff's laundry-basket) and a trailer loaded with dozens of cylinders of compressed hydrogen. From the cylinders, pipes led to a main collector-tube which vanished underneath the circle. It all looked so primitive that I began to have second thoughts about the ride. A man called Fletcher took a minute off from bustling round, supervising the inflation, and introduced himself. He said he was to be the captain of the balloon.

Four at a time the cylinders were turned on and the gas rushed through the collector-pipe. By degrees the fabric rose, looking exactly like an outsize, striped cottage-loaf. Slowly it lifted until at last, by lunch-time, the enormous globe, over thirty feet in diameter, was fully inflated and straining at its net. Fletcher had the basket moved underneath, and fastened it to the many cords hanging down. Almost casually he said, " Do you know that this basket is over twenty years old?" Then, seeing the look of horror on my face, he added, " But I believe it to be quite safe. There are straps which go right round from the cords on either side, under the floor of the basket. So, if it creaks a bit, don't worry, and even if the wickerwork does collapse, we should not fall through."

As the time for take-off approached, Fletcher drilled us carefully: " You will see that the basket has a lot of sand-bags in it. First, I will get in and then take out an equivalent weight of bags. They weigh forty pounds each. Next, the Group Captain will get in, and I will take out more bags. Lastly, we will do the same for you. This will leave us slightly heavier than air. The crew will then walk us to the take-off point. Whatever you do, don't get out without warning. Someone once did this to me because he had forgotten something. The balloon tore up like a bubble, flattened like a mushroom all the way. I was at five thousand feet before I could balance it up again!" We nodded nervously. As far as I was concerned, nothing would have induced me to do anthing whatever without ample warning, primarily in case it strained the basket, in which I had little faith. One by one we got in as he had directed.

When Fletcher had adjusted the balance of the balloon, half a dozen men, each with one hand on the basket, lifted the whole contraption, including the three of us, with no more trouble than they would have had in carrying one shopping-basket between them. Fletcher explained that he used six men, not to lift the basket, but to hold it down if a gust of wind came. I was thankful that it was a calm day. Stepping briskly, the crew walked us across the field to the spot Fletcher had chosen for the ascent, and from which we were least likely to become entangled in any obstruction if there should be drift as we rose. There they put us down.

Fletcher told the crew to stand clear. He picked up a sand-bag and slowly he poured out sand. Suddenly I realised that we were a few inches above the ground and drifting very gently sideways. Fletcher let out more sand. As we began to rise, Steve leaned over the edge of the basket and shouted down to the crew, " Don't you forget that if this device does not come down properly, I am entitled to six Group Captains to carry my coffin at the funeral! " I thought this a very poor joke. However, it delighted the crew and there was a gust of laughter. I found it quite astonishing ; there we were, airborne, and I could hear what people on the ground were saying.

In about five minutes we had reached 1200 feet and Fletcher let out a little gas to stop the ascent. At height there was a gentle breeze of five to seven knots and, peering over the edge of the basket, we could distinguish our gentle and silent movement across the countryside. I could hardly believe my senses. Although we could talk perfectly normally we did not say much, it was so entertaining to listen to the multitude of sounds that came from down below. I had never realised how many of the world's sounds are deadened and lost among intervening obstacles or drowned by the wind. We, drifting, had no wind and nothing between us and the sounds. We heard a man sawing wood about three or four fields away ; a tractor was ploughing and we could hear the put-put-put of its exhaust and the clank of metal as it moved ; we picked out the tune an errand-boy was whistling as he bicycled along a road ; we saw people running out of their houses as we floated overhead, and heard them talking. An aeroplane flew underneath us and it was disturbing to hear the roar of an aircraft's motor coming from *below*. In the balloon we had a walkie-talkie radio set so as to keep in touch with a car which was to follow us until we landed. We could talk to the driver, but neither Steve nor I was able to pick the car out from the dozens of others we could see. We argued about it for some time till Fletcher said, in the pitying tone of voice that is sometimes used to explain simple facts to children, "Why don't you ask him to blow his horn three times?" This was duly passed over the radio and, as the triple note came up from below, we all said together, "There he is!"

Fletcher had, of course, done this many times before, but both Steve and I were soon behaving like little boys. We shouted down from the balloon to people working in the fields. We inquired after the state of their crops, offering gratuitous comment on how they looked from above. A man shouted up to us, "Where are you going to land, because I want to try and get there first?" He seemed quite put out when we answered that we had no idea, for it depended entirely where the wind drifted us. It was easy to see the roads ahead and, switching off the radio, we could yell to our escort car something like '. . . wait by the third house on the left after you pass a pub called the "Rose and Crown." We will drift over there, and we'll give you more instructions then!' Whenever we shouted, tremendous echoes would come rippling back from all round us. The stillness of the air up there and the complete and utter silence were positively eerie. The creaking of the basket as we moved our feet sounded like machine-gun fire. I have flown often, and it was a wonderful change to be low enough to see the country-side closely, and to have time to study it—instead of whizzing past it at breakneck speed.

At last the time came to descend. Fletcher pulled the cord which would let gas out of the valve on the top of the balloon. We could feel the basket beginning to sink, even before his special instruments showed it. When we had reached about five hundred feet Fletcher said, " I think this will do for the moment, till we can see a suit-able landing-place in our path." I always had visions of balloonists throwing out sand-bags to stop coming down. Not so. Fletcher picked up a small handful of sand and, holding it over the edge of the balloon, let about a quarter of it run through his fingers—perhaps a couple of ounces. The descent stopped. The rest of the handful he put back in the bag. He had perfect and most delicate control for up and down, even though he had no control what-ever from side to side. He explained that the balance is so sensitive that, if you were to drop, for example, a camera overboard, it would probably cause a 500-foot rise while sorting things out and before getting the balloon settled down again.

When Fletcher saw suitable terrain ahead he lowered a 250-foot rope under the basket—it was a little thicker than a washing-line. He explained that he would be let-ting out some more gas till about half the rope trailed on the ground ; then he would stop. If the balloon went lower, there would be less weight because of more rope on the ground, so the balloon would go up again. If it went too high, the rope would pull it down. In this way, the balloon would drift gently along, a little more than a hundred feet above the ground, above the trees and buildings in which it might get caught, following the contours, up hill and down dale. Then, when Fletcher was sure of his landing-spot, he could pull the valve and down we would go.

Drifting at a hundred feet was even more delightful, for we could see the spectators' faces. It was easy to see the looks of utter incredulity and to hear their startled remarks. Luckily we did not have a women aboard to hear what some of the men said!

At last Fletcher chose his landing-area. Just before we reached the near boundary of the field he pulled the valve and held it down. We began to sink. " Grip onto the rear edge of the basket," he said, " and bend your knees as we touch. The basket will probably fall over. In this way you will not hurt yourself. Do not, whatever you do, face forwards or you will be thrown down on your nose. " This," he added unnecessarily, " is extremely painful." As it turned out, the wind was so light that the basket came down with only a slight thump, no worse than jumping off a kitchen chair, *and* it stayed upright. " Don't get out," Fletcher added hastily, " till we have lost a lot more gas. If you do, the other two will be whisked up into the air again."

We stood there, three people in a laundry-basket in the middle of a field, feeling rather ridiculous as people ran towards us from every direction. Our only difficulty was in trying to stop them from smoking near the balloon. Thousands of cubic feet of hydrogen were pouring from it. They seemed to take it as a personal insult when

Fletcher suggested that if the mixture caught fire it would blow them into the middle of next week. I felt that their grandfathers and grandmothers would have been more circumspect in a similar situation.

II

Night-flying has a peculiar fascination. It is because you have to take so much on trust. In the daytime you can see where you are going and your senses record exactly what is happening. You work accordingly. At night, when flying, you are completely divorced from anything except the instruments and the lines of lights that show where the ground must be. You cannot see the ground at all except when there is a bright moon, or when a landing-light is used (which is very rare). Yet an aircraft must be flown exactly as if it was broad daylight, for aircraft will only fly in one way. They take no heed of light or dark.

Imagine, if you will, driving a car without headlights very fast along a road. The accelerator is stuck and it is impossible to slow down. Luckily, you have been assured that the road is clear and, where it narrows, there are little lights like cats'-eyes on either side to mark the kerbs. In places, however, when the road is broad enough, there are no cats'-eyes and you must rush on in the inky blackness. It would be, I submit, a somewhat peculiar sensation. You would want desperately to *see* that the way ahead was free from obstructions—just to be sure— but you would have to continue. I get a similar kind of feeling when I night-fly, although many years of flying have stopped it from being disconcerting. It is intriguing, and if the night is right, it can be most beautiful.

Shortly before midnight I nosed the Meteor out of the dispersal point. Ahead of me there were two little bars of light waving in the darkness, telling me what to do. They were special torches and between them, although I could not see him, an aircraft marshaller moved and he was guiding me as I taxied out. By pointing one bar at the port wheel and rotating the other he would be saying, ' swing the aircraft to the left.' Rotating both together told me to come straight ahead. When he had led me out to the taxi-track I turned down it towards the end of the runway. The taxi-track is marked with little lights, orange on one side and blue on the other. The double line stretched away into the distance and I allowed the aircraft to roll down the space between.

At the entrance to the runway I stopped and did my final checks for take-off. All were satisfactory and I asked control for permission to take-off. Having got it I entered the runway and lined the aircraft up, pointing along its length. On each side, stretching away into the distance for over a mile, was a line of lights, each one fifty yards from the next. Except for that, everything above, below and on either side was just darkness. I put the brakes on and began to ease the throttles open. Having checked that full power was coming from each engine, I released the brakes. The five tons or so of thrust from the two engines urged the aircraft down the runway. The converging lines of the flarepath seemed to open as we sped down the middle. Out of the corners of my eyes the pairs of lights could be seen, flicking out of sight, ever faster. Soon the aircraft lifted and the runway lights began to drop away. I selected ' wheels up '. At the same moment I stopped looking outside and concentrated solely on the instruments. To one side of the instrument-panel the colours of the undercarriage indicator were changing: from green to red as the wheels unlocked and then, one-two-three, they went out as the wheels locked 'up'. The instruments told me the machine was in a gentle climb and soon it was nearing three hundred miles an hour.

Outside the cockpit, apart from an occasional speck of light on the ground, which was dropping rapidly away, there was nothing to be seen at all. I was in a world of my own. In front of me was the block of instruments. The luminous paint glowed abnormally bright under the influence of the ultra-violet lights which shone on them from beneath the cockpit coaming. Faintly I could hear the whine of the jet engines and the hiss of the wind. One's natural senses—even the sense of balance—have to be rigidly suppressed because they are so unreliable—they cannot tell one anything that may be trusted. Only the instruments could tell me what the aircraft was doing in relation to the earth below because I had learned to read and accept implicitly their message.

For a few moments after take-off there were occasional farmhouse lights to be seen outside the cockpit. Then, when the altimeter read two thousand feet, they vanished suddenly and I knew we had entered cloud. This could be confirmed by looking out towards the wing-tips, where there was a red-and-green glow from the port and starboard navigation lights shining against the mist on either side. With that odd sense of immobility that one gets in cloud, the climb continued steadily. Methodically I was scanning the instrument panel, each dial in its proper turn and then back to the beginning again. At ten thousand feet the stars appeared overhead. We had come out of the top of the cloud layer.

When the altimeter read thirty thousand feet, about fifty or sixty miles from take-off, there were patches of lights to be seen below. This showed that we were running away from the clouds and into clearer weather. But, by the time forty thousand feet had been reached and there was more than a hundred miles behind, the night had become one in a thousand. The air was clear as crystal, and down below could be seen the night face of half England. There was no sight of the ground itself. It was like looking down on a limitless expanse of black velvet, soft and deep. As a spider's-web in the early dawn, with its thousand droplets of dew catching and reflecting the light, so looked each town, only infinitely more beautiful—a myriad gems laid delicately on the velvet. The lines of the streets could be picked out by the little points of lights—the street-lamps. The streets themselves were invisible. Some rows of lights were blue, some orange and others looked like sparks of diamonds. At some points in the town specks and flashes of red and green could be seen as advertisements gave their messages to passers-by. In between the thousands of little lines, the shape of the town itself appeared to be a phosphorescent green. It was easy to see where the built-up areas ended. I do not know why buildings should appear a green or misty-blue colour, but perhaps it has some connection with the millions of house and shop lights shining from the windows on to lawns and slaty pavements. Most towns were little illuminated webs on their own, but sometimes a thread would run from one to another where big towns lay close together, as in the Midlands. As this fantastic sight sank in, I began counting the towns and identifying them on my map—Birmingham, Wolverhampton, Coventry, Worcester, Gloucester, Liverpool, Oxford. . . . I lost count of them all. All those towns to be seen at one time. It was almost incredible. Back over my shoulder, in the direction of London, there was just darkness. There must have been cloud between me and the city.

In a single-seater there is, in some respects, a distinct sensation of solitude as one sits in the cockpit, apparently almost motionless and eight miles from the nearest house, tree, human being or blade of grass. On the other hand, there is an incessant radio chatter of flying business pouring into one's ears from the many other aircraft in the air and ground-stations on watch. One might suppose that it would be quiet at night: far from it. If you listen from forty thousand feet, from which height you seem to be able to hear everyone, it is as though the air must be stiff with people flying. I listened for a long time to an American team doing practice ground-controlled approaches, talking aircraft down on to the ground and telling them what to do as they watched them by radar. The controller who was doing the talking was particularly good at his job. From his crisp instructions I could visualise most clearly the pilot's actions in successive aircraft and just what they were doing at any instant. The G.C.A. team worked many different aircraft from different places; for, as each practice was complete, the pilot would come on the air with a word of thanks. All kinds of voices were to be heard—Irish brogue, Cockney, American, Scottish and even best B.B.C. Always the controller would come back with a rich Southern drawl, saying, " Thank *you* for your co-operation, suh ; it has been most pleasant to have you with us, and we hope you will come again. Good-night to you, suh, and a good journey home." A delightful human touch in a deadly serious business.

At Shrewsbury I turned towards Middlesbrough and Newcastle. I could hardly believe my eyes as I looked at each of the little spiders'-webs of lights below and ahead of the aircraft. One by one I counted them on the map. Liverpool, which could be identified because the lights stopped suddenly to its left—that must be the sea ; Manchester, Blackburn, Bradford, Leeds, and far beyond that some more lights which stopped abruptly. Could that really be my next turning-point and the sea again on the other side of England, far ahead? Perhaps it was a layer of cloud hiding the lights. Another check. From where I was to Bradford—about sixty miles—the lights stopped roughly the same distance again beyond Bradford. It *must* be Middlesbrough itself, nearly a hundred and fifty miles away. This was no navigation exercise: it was just a joy-flight!

I tucked the map into the pocket of my flying-overalls and settled down to enjoy myself for twenty minutes till we reached Middlesbrough. That night, with most of England laid out below me, it was firmly brought home to me that my detailed knowledge of geography was rudimentary. It was most confusing trying to decide the identity of each town. Bolton, Blackburn and Preston sat in a little clutch, and the map had to come out again to settle which was which. Blackpool was easy—it was more brightly lit and, of course, it was on the coast. The most northerly place that I saw was Edinburgh ; it could be seen from the vicinity of Leeds: later, from the coastline at Middlesbrough, although it was a little closer, it was hidden by clouds round Newcastle.

At Middlesbrough it was southwards once more on a heading for base. By the time we were abreast of Hull the cloud had closed in underneath and the magic of the lights below was past. For all that could be seen, the aircraft might as well have been over a blackboard. Not having to shine through that part of the atmosphere which lay below, the stars above were amazingly brilliant and numerous.

As base approached I thought of the late supper which would be ready for me after landing. In prospect it seemed most delicious, even if it was to come straight from a frying-pan wielded by a tired and bored cook. Soon, under the orders of the controller, the aircraft was plunging earthwards, tearing off the thousands of feet. My relaxation was so complete that, when we entered cloud I was not expecting it. I jumped like a startled rabbit when there was a sudden flash of red and green as the navigation lights lit the mist beside me. Usually, red and green lights close by mean a risk of collision with another aircraft. That was the end of all reveries!

At last we broke cloud and entered the circuit. As the undercarriage indicator lights up, one-two-three, a vivid green, a thought of gratitude went up to the gremlins who fly with all pilots. Even they had not conspired to give trouble. In a few moments the flare-path was lined up ahead. Gradually the lights came nearer and, as the twin lines levelled out on either side, a gentle back-pressure on the stick held them there. Complete and utter blackness, except for the double row of light spots to reassure me that the runway *must* be between them. Speed was dropping off and the wheels settled gently onto something hard. Hundreds of times that has happened, but it never stops being an odd feeling, sliding several tons of machinery at a hundred miles an hour on to something you cannot see. As the brakes came on, the lights on either side passed less and less quickly and finally slowed up to walking-pace. I turned off the end of the runway at the last pair of lights and into the space between the orange and blue rows.

Having taxied in, stowed the aircraft in the hangar, signed up the log-books, put away my flying gear and eaten my meal, I drove home to sleep out what was left of the night.

['Maga' February 1956.

3

SUN TAN 27
Nosmo

The Wing Commander Flying at Driffield, which is a
jet Advanced Flying School in the East Riding, returned
to his office after lunch on an afternoon in late October.
He was not in a good humour. There had been a spell
of bad weather for the last few days and very little pro-
ductive solo flying had been done by his pupils. He had
just been over to the Met. Office to study the latest
weather chart, and it was not encouraging. From Driffield
to the east coast the visibility was down to about 1000
yards, but there was a slight improvement inland. The
Met. Officer had said, however, that there might be a
clearance from the west later in the afternoon.

After pondering for a moment the Wing Commander
pressed his bell for the Flying Wing Adjutant—

" Ring through to the Squadrons," he said, " and tell
them dual flying and continuation training only for the
present. You might also ask the Standardisation Flight
to get an actual weather report from the west: we may
be able to get in some pupil solo later in the afternoon if
a clearance really does develop from that direction."

As a result of this order the Squadron Commanders

detailed the instructors to take their pupils up on various dual exercises to conform to the different stages of training which they had reached. The Standardisation Flight, on the other hand, arranged a continuation training programme, which meant that the instructors were flying by themselves. This Flight is an integral part of every Advanced Flying School: it consists of a number of the highest category flying instructors whose function it is to make certain that all the instructors on the station are continually kept up to the required standard. In order to do their job properly they have to seize every opportunity, in all weathers, to keep in full training themselves.

In a few minutes a number of Mark 7 Meteors, the dual type, were lining up to take off. In the Standardisation Flight two of the pilots detailed to fly were the Flight Commander, Flight Lieutenant Chapman, and Flight Sergeant Wood. These two were to fly single-seater Mark 4 Meteors.

Flight Sergeant Wood was to do a weather reconnaissance below cloud-base to the west of Driffield in accordance with the Wing Commander Flying's orders: he was then to climb into cloud to do some instrument flying up to 20,000 feet, finishing up with a controlled descent through cloud. He was then again to report on any weather improvement by R/T. Shortly after 2.30 P.M. he taxied out and took off. As he climbed through the murk he called the Control Tower—

" Sun Tan 27 proceeding on weather recce to west of sector. Will call you later."

Having received acknowledgment he turned to the west, still climbing. He levelled off at 3000 feet, throttled back to cruising revs. and started to look round him. At this height he was out of the ground mist and noticed that the cloud-base was well above him in the region of 8000 feet. Directly below him he could see the ground flashing past, but when he looked sideways at an angle the fields were hidden in mist. As he flew on, however, the visibility improved, and in a very few minutes he could see the city of York ahead with the beautiful Minster rising out of it. He then turned south towards Selby and tried to gauge the strength and exact direction of the wind from smoke on the ground. Towards Selby the visibility again deteriorated, so he turned north to check the area beyond York. Flying along the very straight railway-line from York to Thirsk he reached Linton-on-Ouse and decided that the wind, although from the right direction, was not strong enough to improve the visibility at Driffield before nightfall.

Since he was now about forty miles from base, and fairly low, he decided to turn on to a homing course before transmitting his weather report so that his R/T message would be stronger. He banked his Meteor into a maximum rate turn to starboard and pulled back slightly on his control column to tighten up the turn. He was flying at about 260 knots, and was watching his direction indicator moving gradually round towards the 120° bearing on which he would straighten out. Just as he was about to complete his turn the aircraft gave a violent shudder and the nose started to drop. At the same moment he was horrified to discover that his rudder was locked solid, and that his control column would move neither backwards nor forwards. He managed to level the aircraft by moving his stick over to the left, but the nose was still down and he was losing height rapidly. After pulling on his stick, and kicking his rudder pedals without effect, he reached forward and tried to pull back on the tail trimmer wheel, which normally gives additional fore-and-aft control. To his consternation the trimmer wheel was also locked solid.

Flight Sergeant Wood's altimeter now registered slightly below 2000 feet and the needle was gradually unwinding as the aircraft approached the ground. The only form of control left to him, apart from his ailerons, was his engines, which he now opened up to full revs. To his intense relief the nose gradually began to rise towards the horizon. The extra thrust from his Derwent engines was overcoming the nose-down attitude of his aircraft. The nose continued to rise with the increased power and the horizon dropped away as the Meteor started to climb. In this attitude the speed began to drop off, and by adjusting his engine revolutions Wood managed to keep his aircraft in a gradual climb at 250 knots.

Wood now had time to appreciate his unenviable position. Although it was infinitely better than it had been a few seconds previously, when he was diving for the ground with apparently nothing to stop him, he was still in a serious jam. His only method of control was by engines and ailerons. So far as his life was concerned he was fairly well placed, since he was rapidly gaining height and could take to his parachute, but he noticed for the first time that trickles of sweat were running down his face from under his flying-helmet, and his hands were clammy inside the white kid flying-gloves. The nervous strain of the last few seconds had asserted itself physically without his realisation.

Wood could not imagine why his controls had jammed, but he was certain that there must have been some failure in the tail unit. His aircraft was still vibrating continuously. While he was initiating his distress call to Driffield he loosened the safety-harness so that he could turn slightly in his seat to look round behind him. Out of the corner of his left eye he saw through the humped perspex canopy that the greater part of his port elevator had broken away and was bent downwards at an acute angle.

Conditions in the Control Tower at Driffield that afternoon were quieter than usual; for there were no pupils flying solo, and the air traffic intensity was consequently light. The local Controller was plotting aircraft in and out of the aerodrome circuit, and the Approach Controller was watching the screen of the cathode-ray tube. In charge, and supervising the whole team, was the Senior Air Traffic Control Officer.

The Approach Controller was in contact with Flight Lieutenant Chapman who was doing a maximum rate descent through cloud, under the call sign of Sun Tan 81. Chapman was a very experienced instructor and the instrument-flying examiner for the School. Now he was coming down from a height of 30,000 on a limited instrument panel to keep his hand in for flying under the most rigorous blind-flying conditions. Most pilots find it difficult enough to do a maximum rate descent through cloud with all their instruments functioning properly, but an examiner has to be able to fly his aircraft to its absolute limits. Each time Chapman transmitted, a thin green line flicked across the screen in the Control Tower giving the exact bearing of the aircraft from Driffield.

Suddenly Flight Sergeant Wood's distress call cut through the Control Room loudly and clearly—

" MAYDAY, MAYDAY. THIS IS SUN TAN 27. MAYDAY."

Everybody in the Tower became rigid, listening intently, with eyes turned to the Approach Controller.

He flicked on his transmitter and, in the same even voice he had been using to Chapman, called—

TOWER: "Go ahead 27. Strength 5."
27: "My elevator has jammed. Position near Linton-on-Ouse. I am climbing at 5000 feet."
TOWER: "Have you any control?"
27: "Only lateral. My rudder and trimmer are also jammed. Speed 250. Still climbing."
TOWER: "Steer 120° for base."

At this point the telephone operator called the Station Commander and Wing Commander Flying to report at once to the Tower. In the meantime all the other aircraft from Driffield, including Chapman, had heard the May-day call and ceased to transmit.

27: "Turning slowly on to 120°."
TOWER: "Fuel?"
27: "Plenty of fuel. 110-120 gallons."
TOWER: "Wing Commander Flying is on his way to Tower. Can you give us any further information?"
27: "A bit of my elevator on port side has broken off and is bent down at an angle."
TOWER: "What is your height now?"
27: "Height 7000. Can you get someone up quickly to have a look at my tail? Throttling back to maintain this height under cloud-base."

At this point Flight Lieutenant Chapman, who had dropped below cloud and had been listening intently, cut in—

81: "Chapman speaking. Can I help? Present position north of base below cloud."
TOWER: "81 steer 220° at 7000 feet to intercept 27."
27: "Request steer."
TOWER: "27 steer 110° and try to maintain 7000 feet. Following is a broadcast to all remaining Sun Tan aircraft— Change frequency to Flying Training Command Guard on channel 'C' to leave this frequency clear for distress procedure. Acknowledge on 'C' Charlie."

81: " I can now see 27 at 7500. Is he steering 110°?"

TOWER: " Sun Tan 27 is steering 110°."

27: " What is your position 81?"

81: " I am quite close and overhauling you."

27: " Roger. Height 7000 at 240 knots."

81: " I am now in formation with 27."

TOWER: " Roger. Both steer 090° for base."

81: " Your port elevator is broken about half-way along its length at the outer hinge and bent downwards and inwards and is bearing hard against your rudder."

27: " Thanks. Now I am beginning to understand. Don't come too close in case I have to abandon suddenly."

81: " Sorry. I will keep wide."

27: " If I could break that bit off I would get back my elevator control and rudder too."

81: " I do not advise you to try to break it off. Something else may come adrift."

TOWER: " Have you any elevator control at all?"

27: " There is very slight reaction if I start forcing hard on the stick, but practically imperceptible."

81: " I advise against undue forcing of control column. You may break something else."

27: " Roger. Is the Wing Commander Flying in the Tower? Ask his advice."

TOWER: " The Wing Commander says you should abandon your aircraft unless you feel you can attempt a landing at Carnaby on the crash-landing strip. If you have any doubt you should go over the side."

27: " Roger. I'll think it over. We want to know what's gone wrong or else this may happen to some other mug."

TOWER: " The Wing Commander says you are not repeat not to land here. The runway is too short. Don't try to land anywhere but Carnaby."

27: " Roger."

TOWER: " Present position?"

27: " West end of main runway. 81 is with me. Ought I to try the stalling speed?"

81: " I strongly advise not. You may spin off it."

27: " I am going to try to reduce speed with 1/3 flap and dropping the undercart. Don't come too close."

81: " Roger. Hauling off."

27: " Maintaining 180 knots with undercarriage and 1/3 flap."

27: " I am going to attempt a landing at Carnaby. Any crash waggon there?"

TOWER: "Bridlington ambulance and fire brigade are already on their way out to Carnaby."

27: "I am orbiting base in a wide circuit. My fuel state is 80 gallons in each tank. Request course to steer for Carnaby."

TOWER: "Steer 065°."

27: "Letting down gradually towards Carnaby. Speed 195 knots. Are the crash waggons ready? Request wind at Carnaby."

TOWER: "Rescue party will be there before you. Wind speed will be same as here, 10 knots easterly.

81: "I am staying with 27 as long as my fuel will allow."

During the war three emergency crash-strips were built at considerable expense to accept damaged aircraft returning from raids over Germany, and for major diversions in bad weather. These are wide tarmac strips, 3000 yards long and 75 wide, with clear approaches. They are situated near the east coast at Manston, Woodbridge and Carnaby. If ever the taxpayer's money has been spent to good purpose, it was on these strips, which have saved so many lives and aircraft in their time. In this particular incident it was indeed fortunate that Carnaby, near Bridlington, was so close to Driffield. All the jet pilots in the Yorkshire area are acutely aware of its position.

Because of his perilous position Flight Sergeant Wood had been given full permission by his Wing Commander to bale out. It was one thing to fly his damaged Meteor within fine limits high up, where he had the chance to abandon it if things went wrong: it was quite another to try to land it. As he approached the ground he would have to discard any idea of using his parachute, and his judgment with such restricted control would have to be meticulous in the extreme. For whereas it is normally necessary to throttle back the engines of an aircraft when flattening out to land, Wood now would have to put on full power to raise the nose of his aircraft. He would have to keep lined up with the runway on the approach without the use of a rudder ; furthermore, his approach speed would have to be very high.

Wood had considered all these points and, after weighing up his chances, elected to try to land his Meteor intact. His chief reason was the feeling that if he abandoned his aircraft the evidence of his elevator failure might be lost, and the cause remain a mystery. The same thing might then occur again with a pilot less experienced than himself, possibly a pupil, and the consequences might be disastrous. His decision was a courageous one.

As Wood approached Carnaby he gradually dropped height by throttling back his engines. When his nose dropped too far below the horizon he brought it back to the correct rate of descent by extra power. At the same time he had to try to pick up features on the ground to guide him to Carnaby in the poor visibility which continued to decrease as he lost altitude. Luckily it had improved a little during the afternoon and was now up to about 2000 yards, but at 195 knots he had to think quickly, and he could only turn very slowly, using ailerons alone. There was no flying control at Carnaby to give him bearings, for this crash-landing strip is not manned. At 1500 feet he picked up the Driffield-Bridlington road which runs by Carnaby and continued to lose height. A moment later he could see the strip ahead, but to his disappointment he was too high and it flashed under him as he opened up his engines to make another attempt. He glanced at his fuel gauges during the very wide circuit that he had to make: they registered 60 gallons in each tank. Now, on top of his other troubles, he had the time factor to contend with because jet aircraft eat up fuel at low altitude, and he wondered if he could afford to go round again more than once if he missed the strip. Running out of fuel at that height would mean certain death.

As he came round in a wide circle to pick up the Bridlington road again he started to lose height earlier, and came down to 1000 feet in the murk. He was determined not to overshoot again, and if he could only sight the Carnaby strip in sufficient time he could do a slight turn to line up. Flight Lieutenant Chapman, who was following him, was becoming anxious, particularly as there was now nothing he could do to assist. He transmitted—

81: "Anything I can do to help?"
27: "Don't think so. I may get in this time."
81: "I'll go ahead."
27: "Roger."

Flight Sergeant Wood continued the wide circuit, keeping his rate of turn constant throughout by reference to his instruments. This would bring him back to the Carnaby strip if his flying was sufficiently accurate. Directly his compass needle reached 80°, the runway heading, he straightened out and dropped his speed to 180 knots, which was as low as he dared. This put his nose well down and he was losing height fast. At 500 feet he was just considering opening up to go round again when, to his relief, he saw the long strip in front of him but slightly to port. He banked to the left, bringing the expanse of tarmac straight ahead, and in a few seconds he was rushing at the runway threshold. As he reached the height to flatten out, at about 20 feet above the ground, he opened up both engines to full power with his left hand and applied full flap with his right. As the nose came up, Wood cut both engines and selected air-brakes out. The Meteor hit the ground at once on three wheels and streaked down the runway. He let her run for a couple of hundred yards and then started applying his brakes. She gradually reduced speed and eventually came to rest in 2500 yards without damage, to the chagrin of the Bridlington fire brigade, who had nearly wrecked their equipment in their spirited and successful effort to get to the air-strip on time.

As Wood turned his aircraft round to taxi slowly back, a Meteor screamed over his head on its way back to Driffield and he heard his Flight Commander's voice in his ears—

" Nice work 27."

Shortly after Wood had switched off his engines the Chief Technical Officer, who had come over from Driffield, inspected the tail unit. It was found that the loss of elevator and rudder control had been caused by the complete fracture of a hinge, which allowed the outer portion of the elevator to fold under and to come in contact with, and jam, the rudder.

As a result of this incident, action was immediately taken to prevent the possibility of such a failure recurring, and in the New Year's Honours List the name of Flight Sergeant Anthony Wood appeared as the recipient of a well-deserved Air Force Medal.

[' Maga ' April 1954.

4

SUNDAY DAWN, SUNDAY DUSK
D. E. Charlwood

Before sunrise, down in the pale, clean fog of the valley, we heard a bugler play reveille. I wondered if he too was in fog, or if from the high hill of the police depot he could look instead across the sunlit upper surface stretching far down the Goroka Valley.

I had been in Goroka for less than two days, but its cycle of weather already seemed familiar: early fog, clear mid-morning, an afternoon of cumulus cloud and a temperature between sixty and eighty. I found it difficult to imagine the coming evening when I would swelter in Madang, five thousand feet down, between the Bismarck Sea and the jungle.

When I left for the control tower the fog was in flight up the dark mountains. Here and there it fought rearguard actions in gorges and hollows, but each moment the day grew brighter and warmer. I walked between beds of poinsettias across close-cut grass, exulting again in the peace and beauty of the valley. The long range of mountains beyond the aerodrome was coming into sight under rising cloud, but the forested slopes of Mount Otto were in shadow. On a grassy hill behind the town I saw again the neat hut of the old native who in his youth had eaten man-flesh and had shared man-flesh with sons now scarcely in middle age. In the dustless air it seemed that one step could take me to the hut door. It was a Sunday, and I was reminded strongly of Sunday mornings of my boyhood when the sea was still and the beach deserted, and the gulls were the only beings in motion.

In the tower Ron was already on duty, his red hair blazing like a beacon in the first light, his eyes puckered. He said, " If you want to get an idea of Highland flying you may be able to go in that Otter."

I went to the windows and looked on to a sturdy, heavy-looking aircraft with a single engine. Natives wearing *lap laps* were loading a complete mobile welder on to it, shouting at each other urgently, getting in each other's way until it looked as if the welder would roll back and amputate bare feet.

" I suppose the pilot will make sure that thing's loaded properly."

" They don't run any risks in these parts," said Ron sententiously.

The pilot climbed to the tower and demanded a weather report for the Wahgi Valley and ' a cup of your coffee '. He had the sharp, slightly testy expression of a man who habitually suspects trouble and is going to outwit it. Ron introduced me. I was from Central Office in Melbourne ; I wanted to see flying conditions in New Guinea. Could I go in the Otter?

" That should be okay," said the pilot. " Yes, that should be okay. There are four other chaps to come and there's the welding-plant—we're allowing a thousand pounds for that. But we'll fit you in."

By now the natives had succeeded in getting the plant

into the aircraft. The end of their battle apparently reminded Ron of my apprehensions.

" Would you say pilots up here run risks, Bill?"

" Run risks?" Bill eyed him narrowly. " You run bloody risks here every time you get airborne."

"' Avoidable risks, I mean."

" Oh hell, no—there are too many of the other kind."

The flight was to be to Chimbu, about thirty miles away, then on to Kerowagi, a further fifteen miles, and lastly twenty-two miles to Omkali, or Omkalikaukau. These places lay on the other side of the dividing range we looked on from the control tower, the blue-grey mountains rising between eight and ten thousand feet, their peaks still in cloud.

" I'm afraid you can't go to Chimbu," said Ron. " They haven't sent in their rainfall report."

Bill put his hands on his hips. " That dam' welding-plant is theirs. Can't we raise them?"

" They don't keep a Sunday ' Schedule.' "

" Hmph. The only thing I can do is to drop the welder at Kerowagi and the boys can wheel it through the bush. I'll fly over Chimbu on the way just in case they pass you something."

I turned up the Aerodrome Directory and saw that Chimbu was closed to Otters after a hundred and ten points of rain. It was a grass strip two thousand one hundred feet long, open for one-way operations. Its height was four thousand nine hundred feet. ' Severe cross-winds and turbulence after midday,' said the Directory.

I turned to Kerowagi. It was at an elevation of five thousand two hundred feet and was also a one-way grass strip. These two aerodromes were termed Group ' Y ' standard, which I gathered was a lowly category. When I turned to Omkali I saw that it was categorised 'ALG.' I glanced at the specifications for Authorised Landing Grounds and read: 'ALG are those landing-grounds which by reason of their physical characteristics or the limited scope of operations contemplated, it is not technically possible to develop to Group 'Y' standard, but from which operations are necessary for the development of the Territory. Operations to and from Authorised Landing Grounds are confined to specific types of aircraft only, and all such operations must be conducted at the Operator's risk. The minimum criterion for the authorisation of a landing-ground will be to satisfy the Department of Civil Aviation that operations can be conducted with reasonable safety.'

I turned back to Omkali. 'Elevation 5500 feet,' said the Directory. 'Grassed earth ; length 1800 feet ; one-way operations ; slope 13.4 per cent to the south-east.' I scratched doubtfully at the figure 'one' before I saw a corroborating note: 'Caution: Maintain momentum with power after landing in order to negotiate steep slope '.

" Are you right?" asked Bill.

" Yes," I answered carelessly.

As we walked down the stairs I remarked, " Two engines would be reassuring in this country, I should think."

" If you started worrying about engine failure," said Bill, " you'd never get anywhere in the Highlands. Anyhow, these things stall at thirty-eight knots, so it should be possible to put them on the side of a mountain."

When we stepped outside, I looked towards the creased and naked ranges. The creases were valleys, too steep for trees. The heads of some were filled with ascending cloud. A forced landing there at any rate was out of the question.

There were already three men in the back of the Otter and a fourth beside the pilot. They were sitting with their legs on various crates and packages. They were young men, capable-looking and immediately friendly. Up forward was the recalcitrant welder, pinioned under a net.

We lined up parallel to the mountains and roared across the grass. For a moment I saw the few streets and gardens of Goroka, then they were hidden by cloud. Instrument flying was forbidden, but in conditions like these a few seconds in cloud was unavoidable. We emerged with the mountains noticeably nearer. I could see streams in the valleys now and the native paths on the ridges, then cloud again, wetting the windows, then a waterfall, long and thin.

Beside me was a man of twenty-three or twenty-four. He was going, he said, to Kundiawa, the village beside Chimbu aerodrome.

" I believe we might not land at Chimbu," I said.

He seemed to care very little. " We can go through the bush by Land-Rover," he said.

We were clambering over the top of the range. Cloud trailed in tree-tops slightly below us. The man beside me explained that he was an agricultural officer. He had graduated in Melbourne two or three years before and his main responsibility now was the care of half a million coffee-trees.

" What companies do they belong to?"

" Not to any companies really—they belong to the natives."

Over the range we ran parallel to vertical limestone

ridges. We were now below cloud and below the peaks. Spread before us was the valley of the Chimbu River, the territory of a hundred and fifty thousand natives. Much of the valley floor was patterned by native gardens: the chocolate of freshly tilled earth, the dark green of *kau kau*, the lighter greens of crops unknown to me. At the head of the valley, unconcealed by cloud, stood Mount Wilhelm, rising blue and beautifully proportioned to fifteen thousand five hundred feet.

The forbidden Chimbu airstrip lay green and deserted, its nearby mountains steaming in the sun. Bill ran low over the grass then low over the adjoining village of Kundiawa. Its few buildings and huts climbed a hillside and we loooked on them like a picture hung on a wall for our swift scrutiny: cowering dogs, natives gazing upward, a portly white man, hands on hips. The din of the engine racketed off the face of the hill. Then we were chasing our shadow over the broad, green valley again, heading for Kerowagi. Isolated grass huts lay below and patches of native gardens and a sinuous red road. This was the way the agricultural officer would go by jeep through the bush, and this the way the natives would wheel the welding-plant. Then, in the depths of this wilderness a massive wooden cathedral arose—the Catholic mission of Migende. It was surrounded by such numbers of natives that the ground appeared as if covered by black ants.

"The *popies* are in force this morning," shouted one of the passengers. "They get four or five thousand along each Sunday."

We passed over a high, isolated hill surmounted by a cross. The agricultural officer leaned over to me. "In the 'thirties the natives here killed two missionaries."

Looking on that lonely and eloquent cross, I found myself anxious to learn more, to learn whether this was the site of the missionaries' grave, or the site of the killing, or simply a memorial. And I wanted to know more about the extraordinary change in so short a time in the lives of the four or five thousand black *popies*. But we had already begun descending into Kerowagi and the agricultural officer was gathering up his parcels.

Bill put the Otter down on sundrenched grass beside the mountains. Just off the runway stood a small neat building of the patrol post. Outside it were two white people, a young man and his wife, standing among fifty or sixty natives. Most of the natives wore no more than a scanty string apron and a few decorative beads and arm-bands. Many of the men had a boar's tusk through the septum of their noses, and others carried long, black palm-bows and one or two arrows.

While the natives struggled to unload the Chimbu welding-plant, and Bill worked out his load-sheets, the white man introduced himself. He explained that he and his wife were from Liverpool. It was a far cry from Liverpool to New Guinea, I remarked. Ah, but Kero-wagi, he declared, was the most beautiful station in the Highlands.

I walked to the other side of the solitary building across thick, close-cut grass. In Goroka I had seen natives cutting such grass with broad-bladed knives, stooping and swishing as the mood took them. Alone again, I sat looking across a green and shallow valley. On its other side rose the dividing range between the Sepik and the Wahgi rivers, its highest peaks above twelve thousand feet. Between me and their clouded tops was grassland, like a park which had been cropped by sheep or horses.

But in Kerowagi there were neither sheep nor horses, nor any other domestic animals. Here and there in this undulating parkland were tree-ferns, bursting upwards like fountains, their fronds full of light, and growing in groves, tall, dark-green trees resembling blue-gums. One native hut stood alone, oblong in shape, built of plaited kunai grass. On the edge of the valley someone had planted a long row of poinsettias. They were now in full bloom, scarlet against the many shades of green.

No place I had known possessed the peace of Kerowagi ; no place so quickly induced a desire to be still, to watch and to listen. Perhaps the nearness of the clouds had much to do with it. They marched and countermarched across the peaks, their shadows sweeping the grass. All this in silence. Nor was there any sort of movement in the scene, apart from the movement of the shadows. The air at five thousand feet was bafflingly clear, so that I could not have said whether a particular tree was a mile away or half a mile. I fancied that a sense of extended perception was upon me ; that if I waited long enough in the warm and motionless air, the clouds would make some revelation to me.

Then, along a path near the poinsettias, I saw two men walking slowly, bow in hand. They were dressed alike in ankle-length aprons of *tapa*-bark cloth. Their hair was powdered white and about their foreheads they wore bright-red bands. Below these were second bands, brown in colour, which came low over their eyes. One man had the hair of his chin and cheeks trimmed short and carefully combed and oiled, so that it looked like black grease-paint. Bridging his nose was a white patch. The two walked softly past me, their faces serious, their torsos gleaming.

As there still appeared much for Bill to do, I crossed the aerodrome to a church on its other side. I could hear a native somewhere within preaching an impassioned sermon to an invisible congregation.

Bill put away his papers. " You may as well ride in the cockpit from here on," he said. " You'll get a good look at Omkali—it's the steepest strip in New Guinea."

Natives lined either side of the Kerowagi aerodrome waiting for us to take off. Bill carried out a long cockpit check, then repeated it. He told Goroka his intentions and from beyond the ranges came the controller's acknowledgment. Then we were away, the natives running and waving on either side, the wheels sending a hollow bumping through the fuselage. We climbed steeply, and in a few minutes again passed the high hill and its surmounting cross.

Omkali lay ten minutes away, somewhat east of south. Before long we began following a turbulent stream which ahead of us entered the heart of the mountains. Pointing to this defile, Bill shouted, " The Wahgi Gorge."

At a distance it appeared too narrow to accommodate our wing-span, but we plunged into it, clattering like an express train, the Wahgi foaming below. At the end of this corridor the Wahgi joined another stream almost at right angles, and as far as I could see there was nowhere left for us to go.

" There's the aerodrome," Bill shouted.

I glanced about us. " Where?"

He dropped the starboard wing. " There—just above us."

" I see," I lied. I kept glancing through my window into the steep side of the gorge where natives had contrived to make gardens grow on a sixty-degree slope. I could still see nothing to land on.

Bill climbed a little and began turning to starboard. Only then did I see Omkali. Where the streams formed a ' T,' in the angle of the ' T,' absurdly tipped up, looking nothing like an airstrip, was a chute of grass with a village clinging to its upper end. A mountain rose straight behind the village, its top in cloud. At the approach end was another mountain, separated from the strip by the gorge of the other river. Bill banked against its side and began a short approach.

' This,' I thought, ' is an absurd place for me to be in. I am a man who goes daily to an office with a brief-case. I have a wife, children——'

My feet propped against the floor. The angle of approach felt entirely wrong. I glanced at Bill's face. Presumably he knew what he was doing, but I had never been so close to touchdown in a position so likely to dig a plane into the ground. Blades of grass were visible through the windscreen when the nose went up and our wheels touched. Immediately only mountain and sky were visible. I heard power go on and instinctively looked ahead into the mountain. How could we possibly go round! In the next instant I remembered the warning: ' Maintain momentum with power after landing in order to negotiate steep slope '.

At the top of the slope a shelf had been cut as a parking-place. The Otter clambered on to it and regained an even keel. Bill cut the motor. I was ready to lead the surrounding natives and few Europeans in applause, but Bill was only granted a perfunctory " G'day ".

We were climbing out when air traffic control at Goroka spoke to us: " A Cessna has landed at Chimbu and reports nil rainfall ".

" Roger," said Bill resignedly. " I left their welder at

Kerowagi. I'll call in on the way back and tell them where it is."

Outside I looked back down the steep slope into the cloud-blotched wall of mountain. It was impossible to tell how near the peak was ; in fact impossible to judge any of the distances. I climbed the cutting above the parking-shelf to high ground behind it. Large numbers of native children followed me whispering speculatively and good humouredly. I photographed the Otter, lying well below me though only thirty yards or so distant. On the other side of it, the green landing-strip tapered away between white markers. The strip ran parallel to the gorge, but dividing the two was a narrow ridge. I walked down this ridge, looking on the one hand into the shadowed gorge and on the other, across the grass. The ridge was six or seven feet higher than the strip and divided from it by a deep drain perhaps five feet wide. I was walking above this drain when Bill called from the aircraft that he was ready to leave. In a direct line he was not far from me, but clearly it would take some time if I retraced my steps. I contemplated the drain, wondering whether to leap it and walk straight back. The native children stopped and exchanged low, excited remarks, as if I were about to perform some hazardous feat. Listening, I began to doubt my estimate of distances. Perhaps the drain was twelve feet wide and perhaps I was ten feet above it. In the brilliant sun and translucent air, I might well be misjudging. I held my camera tightly and went to the edge. The whispering rose in a crescendo then died to a serious silence. I leaped and in the thin and heady air described a parabola that bade fair to carry me across the strip. The children cheered wildly and ran back the way we had come.

Bill started up and we tipped over the edge of the shelf. There was no holding the Otter. For a few yards she bolted, then the runway fell from beneath her, leaving her suspended over the grass, then over the gorge, the mountain large ahead. We banked to port and turned into the cross-bar of the ' T,' then down the long arm of the ' T,' flying just below the top of the gorge, the Omkali strip level with our eyes, the people up there waving to us.

" Now I have seen everything," I said.

To reach Chimbu we followed the gorge to the valley of the Chimbu River. Although this aerodrome did not have the slope of Omkali, it was rather similarly placed, beside a deep valley with a side valley to be crossed on the approach. There were two strips, one of them no longer in use.

" A couple of aircraft pranged on take-off from the old strip—couldn't turn in time and hit that mountain."

We bumped again across sunlit grass. Ahead, far up the valley, stood Mount Wilhelm, deep blue and plumed with cloud. As we pulled up, three white men and a crowd of natives came forward to unload the welding-plant. They were having a working bee, they said, and needed to use it. Lengthy explanations and counter explanations followed.

" Ah, *maski* " (forget it), said a plump white man resignedly.

Two District Officers, one from Goroka and one from Lae, had travelled with us. They disappeared now in the direction of the village, leaving us to wait. Bill introduced me to a short, fair man of about thirty, explaining to me that he was a *lik lik* doctor. A *lik lik* doctor, or ' little doctor ', is a man who has been trained to about the standard of a nurse and who carries out medical duties in a remote locality, and sends his difficult cases out by aircraft.

When Bill had seated himself on the grass and was intent upon his load sheets, the *lik lik* doctor came and sat beside me in the sun.

" Really," he explained, " I am not a *lik lik* doctor. I graduated in Sydney. Bill always introduces me as a *lik lik* doctor. I can understand the mistake well enough. He takes a lot of cases out of here that I won't touch— I often suspect gangrene and can't risk keeping a patient here."

" How many patients do you usually have?"

" Oh, Pat and I average about three hundred a day."

Pat was an Irishman and, I gathered, a genuine *lik lik* doctor.

Lying in the sun the doctor talked of fractures and abrasions caused in fights over pigs and land and women ' in that order ', and about young nurses who went out to native villages accompanied only by a police-boy.

Bill put his papers away and lay beside us on the grass. " This would be a pleasant life if there were no paper-work," he said.

Lying in the sun we could see the nearer coarse green blades of grass and, in the same glance, the aerodrome falling into a narrow valley and, beyond that, the high mountain free now of cloud ; all this as still as a picture.

By midday Bill was becoming restive. The two District Officers had not returned from the village. At one o'clock I had hoped to get a ride to Madang ; besides, there was the Aerodrome Directory's warning of afternoon turbulence and cross-winds.

I heard the District Officers before I saw them. " —a

powerful fellow," said one. " Most violent. Broke away from the police-boys."

And the other, raising his voice, said to Bill: " Would you be able to pick up a bad prisoner here this afternoon? There'll be a police-boy with him."

" Okay," said Bill laconically.

We took off into the south-west and turned under the peak of Mount Naru.

" We'll go back over the Daulo Pass. The road crosses the divide there at nine thousand one hundred."

There was cloud still on the divide. From the cockpit I could see the red road, heaving itself coil on coil up the foothills till, among moss-festooned trees, it struggled over the ridge and ran down towards Goroka. The Goroka valley looked warm and friendly and comparatively civilised. There again were the bright gardens under the wall of mountains, and there the aerodrome with its lines of poinsettias, and there the mess where no doubt Nimmi had lunch prepared.

Early in the afternoon a DC3 on a charter flight was returning empty to Madang, sixty miles to the north. The pilot agreed to take me with him. He was, I discovered, an Englisman with the voice and slang of the R.A.F., but a complexion little lighter than the natives'.

" Well, we'll get cracking. Come along up front if you like."

The small town with its streets and its pastel houses quickly receded. Before us were the clouded peaks of the Bismarck Range. We were to pass through them by the Goroka Gap, but its side were both concealed. The two pilots watched the dark-green earth until we were through. Ahead then was a scene of cloud such I had never witnessed. Warm, moist air from the Bismarck

Sea had been forced up by the ranges to form towering cumulus and cumulo-nimbus cloud of tremendous vertical extent, the highest of them corresponding to underlying peaks. For fifteen minutes we wound through white corridors. The undergrowth below us changed from forest to jungle and the air in the cockpit grew warmer and more humid until ahead, by a lethargic sea, lay Madang.

The single strip of the aerodrome ran alongside the jungle towards a palm-fringed harbour. As we came low over the approach path I saw the wartime wreckage of a Boston lying not far from touchdown. Further wreckage lay off the far end of the runway, this a Zero.

On the ground there was no breeze ; indeed, it seemed as if there were no air. A man wearing the usual white shorts and shirt and dark glasses greeted me.

" Where have you booked me, Alan?"

" I'm taking you home," he said.

A strange twist of life had brought Alan Woodward back as a civilian to this, his first operational unit during the war. From here he had flown when he was eighteen and from here, when his multifarious duties as O.I.C. allowed him, he flew still. He stood in sometimes for local Cessna pilots and flew into Omkali and Chimbu and various other Highland aerodromes. Madang was the airport through which these places, and Goroka itself, received all the benefits of civilisation, including houses to live in.

We drove to the town along a white and glaring road surfaced with dead coral. It ran at times against a wall of jungle and finally emerged beside the harbour at the mouth of the Gogol River. Coconut-palms leaned motionless over a viscid sea. A native slowly paddled his *lakatoi* towards a flat cape on which further palms were clustered. His easy strokes and the slight rise and fall of the sea were the only movements visible.

In the town we entered a long and deeply shaded avenue of rain-trees, their pale, smooth trunks bearded with ferns and mosses. Hereabouts, scattered in the shade, were a few shops, some Chinese, some primitive-looking native trading stores. The rain-trees were planted by the Germans during their long-vanished settlement. They built on this site in 1884, and for fifteen years it was the headquarters of the German New Guinea Company under the name of Friedrichwilhelmshafen. Then malaria drove the colonists to found a healthier capital in New Britain.

When I had showered and changed we sat on Alan's screened verandah. There was a booming undertone of waves to our conversation. Not far off stood a tall white lighthouse, designed in the form of a torch of peace but looking rather like a giant rocket awaiting count-down. It was to be dedicated in a few days to the memory of the wartime Coast Watchers of New Guinea. Many of these men had lived locally and a few survivors did so still. When war broke out they worked behind the Japanese lines, usually alone and constantly in danger.

When the day had cooled a little we drove eastward parallel to the shore. The coastline was flat and everywhere there were coconut-palms and unbeautiful kapok-trees. A weary sea collapsed against the shore. There was no sand, only a low, coral declivity. Swimming as a pastime was not considered worth while, the sea being much too warm and the sharks much too attentive. But sport was still available for the energetic, and numbers of enthusiastic golfers were pacing fairways on the opposite side of the road, oblivious of the tepid air.

We turned back to the town to see the last remaining signs of the German settlement. One was simply the date 1913 engraved on the wall of what might have been an administrative building. Others were a few Germanic-looking crosses under the heavy shade-trees of an abandoned cemetery. Nearby I was surprised to find a new headstone, evidently replacing one there formerly. It marked the graves of Karl Boschal, an official of the New Guinea Company, who had been born in Memel in 1861 and died in Friedrichwilhelmshafen in 1913, and of his wife who pre-deceased him. The original memorial was erected by the Company, but who had recently renewed it I was unable to discover.

There were over sixteen hundred Germans in Madang and New Britain, but in 1914 they lost everything. I heard them both praised and disparaged. They were reputedly harsh colonisers, but also reputed to be just. There were older natives who referred still to the good old days of the ' German man ', when apparently right and wrong were clearly defined and punishment was swift.

We drove on westward towards Alexishafen. Bands of natives strolled here and there along the roadside, many of the men with hibiscus flowers in their hair, most of the women in bright, shapeless cotton frocks. On one side of the road interminable coconut plantations grew and on the other, the jungle. I felt the palms oddly wearisome. Their rustling heads were remote above us and in character one differed little from another. But contrasting with their aloof rows was the dim and silent fecundity of the jungle. Trees and palms and vines climbed voraciously on the rotting remains of their predecessors.

Standing in the green shadows it was not difficult to imagine the flitting of a bird to be the swift movement of men in jungle-green. In the jungle, far back in the mountains, the Americans were still recovering the remains of their dead.

We turned once into a private drive through a plantation. Our path was close-pressed by coconut-palms which starred the earth with their shade. Beneath them grew cocoa-trees, with large polished pods hanging under dark-green leaves. We travelled slowly in chequered sunlight, emerging at length into a large clearing where two long sheds stood with roofs no more than eight feet high. Outside the sheds were two flat-topped trucks, perhaps fifteen feet long, which could be wheeled on rails into the sheds. The tops of the trucks were covered with freshly picked cocoa-beans drying in the sun. A European planter and two natives were attempting to lift one of the trucks back on to its rails. We joined the sweating group, and when the job was done, the planter asked us to his home. His plantation ended at an inlet of the sea and there the house stood, its walls almost entirely of mosquito-wire, its eaves wide. Between it and the sea ran a hedge of crotons. About half a mile across the water lay a small island, its palms and jungle ringed by a white beach.

" On that island are the remains of a Lightning," the planter said. " It was hit over Madang and the American pilot ran it up the beach into the jungle. He was badly knocked about—so the natives tell me. They smuggled him back into the mountains before the Japs could find him. They looked after his wounds for some time, but one of the tribe told the Japs of his hiding-place and they came and took him and executed him."

We looked at the island with new eyes, as if all the tension and the concentration of that landing had suddenly been thrust upon us. Now there was only a jungle-grown wreck as a memorial to courage and skill and futility.

" Well," we said uneasily, " It's getting late."

We stood up and, with a backward glance at the island, drove away through the palms.

We arrived in time for dinner and soon it was dark. On the ceiling were several geckos—small, almost transparent, lizards with swivelling eyes and a sharp chirruping cry out of all proportion to their size. Outside, the road lay pale under the moon. The warm sea beat still at the shore. It was, I realised, only twelve hours since I had heard the bugler of the Royal Papuan and New Guinea Constabulary sound reveille above the Highland fog.

[' Maga ' March 1960.

5

TOTEM FLIGHT 347
Jonathan Spence

" Captain Dexter," the co-pilot called, " I'm picking up that front on the radar—it's responding at thirty miles."

The Captain looked up from the navigator's table and moved forward. He leaned over the engineer's shoulder and glanced out. Up ahead he could see the grey wall of cloud, black in patches where it rested on the ocean fourteen thousand feet below, and a lighter grey where it merged with the high overcast above.

" O.K. I'll come up front."

Chuck Knight, the engineer, folded up his jump-seat to let the Captain slide past and ease in behind the left-hand control column.

Paul Dexter was worried. This was turning out to be one of those difficult trips. Before they left London it had seemed pretty straightforward—Flight 347, London direct Montreal, seventy-five passengers, scheduled time eleven hours thirty minutes.

At 5.30 that morning the flight-planning office had called him at his hotel in Richmond with the news that he could not make the flight direct. There were strong headwinds all the way across the ocean. Two hours later in the Met. Office at London Airport he had seen the picture. A low-pressure system in Labrador radiated a complicated system of fronts and occlusions. They spread, like a fan, from the St Lawrence, along the Eastern Seaboard, and well into the Atlantic. All the Maritime stations were forecasting low cloud and poor visibilities in snow.

"The navigator figures we've lost forty minutes," said Dexter, turning towards the co-pilot ; "and what with that hour we lost refuelling at Shannon. . . . I wouldn't mind betting we're at least three hours late into Montreal. Why the company publish a schedule beats me."

The machine shuddered slightly as it encountered the first fringes of turbulence. Dexter switched on the seat-belt sign and peered into the radar screen. He adjusted the brilliance, and altered course slightly to avoid the storm cell that showed up as an ugly yellow blob on the screen.

"Wing and prop de-icers on," said Dexter, nudging the engineer ; "and watch for carb icing."

Damn' foolish, thought Dexter, telling Chuck Knight to watch out for carburettor icing, telling the most experienced engineer in the company to watch out for an elementary thing like that. I'd better watch myself, he thought, otherwise the word will get around that I'm getting jumpy. Perhaps I am. Still—after this trip I can relax.

As the machine plunged into the grey cloud, a curtain of rain struck the front windshield—rattling like lead-shot on a tin roof.

"Number one prop de-icer's no good," shouted Chuck urgently. "I've checked the circuit-breakers."

Dexter looked up and saw that the ammeter needle was reading zero.

" Damn! We'll have to climb. See if you can raise Gander, Scott," he said, turning to the co-pilot. " Get me clearance to climb to twenty or twenty-two thousand feet." Scott was new to the company. He still wanted watching a bit. He looked pale, thought Dexter, but it was probably the light. He certainly looked young compared with Chuck Knight and himself.

The ship was tossing about more violently now. Dexter looked out over the port wing, scrutinising the outboard engine for signs of ice. So far they had not picked anything up, but he felt uncomfortable watching the mainplane and engines flexing through the cold wet cloud.

" I've got our request through, sir," said Scott ; " managed to raise Frobisher—they said stand by."

Dexter nodded his head and switched in his H/F receiver. He could hear a lot of noise in his headset, and then a remote voice gave them clearance. The message had to be repeated twice before they got it completely. Dexter pushed the headset back off his ears.

" O.K., Chuck," he said. " Give me climb power—we're going up to twenty-two thousand."

He watched for a second as the engineer's hands moved throttles and the master pitch lever, as he altered mixture settings and adjusted the engine-cowl flaps. He heard the healthy sound of the engine power surge, and moved the auto-pilot elevator control back. The machine started its laborious climb through the murk. Using the radar screen, Dexter steered to avoid the storm centres. He watched as the altimeter needle slowly crept upwards. At twenty thousand it began to get lighter and soon they were running in and out of wispy stratus cloud, with large black walls of towering cumulus on either side. Finally he levelled out at twenty-two thousand and ordered cruise power. He noticed with satisfaction the low outside air temperature—there would be no icing at this height. High above them the sky was still overcast, but the air was much smoother. Dexter reached up and switched off the seat-belt sign.

"We can't make Montreal direct at this altitude, sir," the navigator shouted across the engineer's shoulder. "I make the new estimate around twenty-two-forty hours— we're going to lose an hour and five minutes at this level. Our gas will run out at about twenty-two-twenty. That includes diversion, and stand-off."

"O.K.," said Dexter. "I guessed as much ; but we've got to stay up here. I'm not risking low level in this weather with number one prop de-icer out. We'll land at Gander and refuel. Weatherwise it's a bit marginal— but if we can't get in, we'll continue to Stephenville— they seem to be holding out O.K."

The navigator returned to his table. Dexter re-trimmed the aircraft, centred the auto-pilot, and switched in the altitude lock.

He had been late before, it was one of those things one had to expect from time to time in the airline business. Man-made schedules for crossing the Atlantic depend upon the whims of the weather, the distribution of pressure systems and the winds. There is nothing that anyone can do about it. The only trouble was that this time he particularly wanted to arrive on time.

Five days before—when he left Toronto for London— he made all the arrangements for his two weeks' vacation. His wife and the two children would be waiting for him at Dorval. As soon as he had cleared customs they were to push off up to the Laurentians. They had rented a cottage by the side of a lake and there was a good ski slope right alongside. He'd planned to do this the previous year, but owing to some extra flights the firm had not given him any spare time until the end of March. By then the best of the snow had gone. They had cancelled it that time. And before then, something had always turned up. One-year-young Johnny got measles. Another time Margaret, his wife, had to look after her mother who had suddenly become ill. Now once again his arrangements had gone awry. He should have been well clear of the airport by four in the afternoon. It would be dark before he even landed at Montreal. He could imagine his wife hanging round the Totem office—the children becoming restless.

"Captain Dexter!"—it was a woman's voice. He looked back to see Mary, the English hostess, standing behind the engineer's seat.

"We're having a bit of trouble with one of the passengers, sir. She seems to think that she's about to have a baby. Could you come and have a look at her?"

Dexter unfastened his seat belt and removed his headset. The engineer folded up his jump-seat to let him by.

"Jees, what next?" he said, and turned to the co-pilot. "You take over, Scott. See if you can pick up some more weather broadcasts."

"Where is this woman?" he asked.

"She's a Mrs Pasquier—French Canadian—in M.3 in the rear compartment. She says she's only seven months on the way. She's had five children before—all before time, but never as early as this. She thinks it was all that bumping about that started it off." The girl replied with the precise clipped speech of an English education, which six months with Totem had not softened.

"Why the hell did London book her if she's in this condition?" said Dexter testily. "Have we got a medical clearance on her?"

"No . . . she didn't say anything about that. She's coming back to Canada to have the child. She's got a through booking to Quebec."

"O.K. I'll have a look at her," said Dexter reluctantly, and followed the hostess back through the first two compartments.

Mrs Pasquier was lying in the aisle between the close-packed rows of seats. Her head was propped on some pillows, and she was covered with a blanket. Her eyes were closed, and Dexter noticed the pallor of her lined face. Her dark hair was streaked with grey, and lay untidily on the pillow. She was not a young woman, well past forty, thought Dexter.

The second hostess was sitting on the arm of the only empty seat in the compartment, looking at the woman with concern. As he approached, she looked up.

"I've given her a sedative, sir," she said. "She's much quieter now."

Dexter was not sure that a sedative was quite the right thing to give an expectant mother. He leaned over, and supporting himself on the back of one of the seats, felt her brow. It was cold and damp.

"We can't have her lying here," he said, standing up and turning to Mary. "We'll have to move her up front. Would you fix up a bed for her on the crew-rest seat? I'll bring her up with Anne."

"Very well, sir," said the girl, "I'll do it right away," and she bustled towards the forward end of the aircraft. Dexter smiled inwardly at her English accent. He was now left with the second hostess.

" Have we got a doctor on the passenger manifest, Anne?" he asked.

" No, we've already checked that. But I'll ask when we've got her fixed up forward."

Mrs Pasquier had opened her eyes. " I'm sorry for all the troubles," she murmured.

" We're taking you up front," said Dexter, " you'll be more comfortable there. Do you think you can stand up?"

Anne held her shoulder as the woman awkwardly lifted herself and, supporting herself on the arm of the nearest seat, stood up. She was very small, thought Dexter. Without a word the woman clung on to Anne, and together they moved slowly towards the front. Dexter picked up the pillows and blanket and followed.

" Say, Cap'n." A thickly dressed crew-cut male passenger grabbed his gold-braided sleeve. " What time are we making Montreal?"

" Around six-thirty," Dexter replied. " We'll have to make a stop at Gander to take on more gas."

" Hell!" said the man, ironically ; " I'm going jet next time!"

Other passengers waylaid him on the way forward, asking questions which Dexter answered with consideration. Maintaining good passenger-relations they called it back at Totem's headquarters in Toronto, and Dexter tried to keep to the standard. Competition was pretty keen on the North Atlantic, and the personal touch sometimes persuaded passengers to travel again with Totem, rather than with their competitors' jet-speed equipment.

By the time Dexter arrived up front again, the woman was lying in the rest-seat with a blanket over her. She looks comfortable enough, thought Dexter.

"See if you can get some sleep," he said.

She nodded in assent, and he noticed with satisfaction that she closed her eyes.

"O.K., Mary," he continued; "go back and start looking after the customers again. They'll probably need buttering up a bit now they know we've got to stop at Gander. I'll call you if the woman starts anything."

The hostess smiled, straightened her jacket, opened the cabin door, and went back to her passengers. Dexter turned his attention once more to the operating of the aircraft. He leaned over the navigator's table and followed through the neatly written log.

"Another hour twenty to Gander," said the navigator. "We should have three hours and fifty minutes' fuel left overhead Gander."

"That sounds O.K.," said Dexter. "With that set-up we can hang around Gander for a good two and a half hours before diverting to Stephenville . . . if the weather at Gander clamps down on us."

He moved up to the front of the cockpit and climbed in behind the control column. He fastened his lap-strap, put on his head-set and called Gander on the H/F frequency. He told them of his intention to land at Gander, and asked for a doctor to meet the aircraft on arrival. He checked over the latest weather reports that Scott had taken down. Conditions at Gander were just above company limits, four hundred feet cloud-base, and a mile visiibility in light snow-showers. Stephenville was still well above limits, he noted with satisfaction.

He checked through the briefing-sheets. The co-pilot took down another weather sequence, and the engineer checked over the instrument readings. Mary managed to find time to bring them each a cup of coffee. She had been round all the passengers: there was no doctor on board, but the woman seemed to be sleeping peacefully.

They had lost another ten minutes by the time they reached the control boundary. Scott called up the Centre and got clearance to descend.

Dexter switched off the altitude lock, and rotated the elevator knob on the auto-pilot. The machine started on its way down. To the south-west a thin orange line showed where the sun reflected the cloud-layers. At eighteen thousand feet they plunged into cloud again. It became darker, and Dexter turned up the panel lights. He looked anxiously at the temperature-gauge, and out towards the outboard engine.

"Prop and thermal de-icers on," he ordered. He looked at the number one ammeter needle—hoping that by some miracle it might have rectified itself—but the needle stayed glued to zero.

"You're cleared to the Gander range at two thousand feet . . . change to approach radar frequency."

Dexter selected the new frequency. "Field approach check," he called, and uncoupled the auto-pilot. He grasped the wheel with both hands and smoothly rode the light turbulence of the enveloping cloud.

"Totem three-four-seven, you are now ten miles from the field," came the clear voice in Dexter's head-set. "You are cleared for a radar approach to runway zero-four. Reduce to approach speed."

He heard Scott acknowledge, and ordered twenty degree flap. He reduced the power and retrimmed the elevator.

"Steer two-five-zero," continued the ground controller. "Descend to two thousand feet."

Dexter eased the machine on to the new heading, riding the intermittent bumpiness in the cloud.

"Wind is from the north at fifteen knots . . . gusting . . ." continued the voice. "Visibility fifteen hundred yards, cloud estimated three hundred feet—you're cleared to land off this approach."

Damn, thought Dexter, visibility has gone down. Right on limits. He watched the altimeter unwind, and at two thousand feet levelled her off.

"Number one engine is running rough!" shouted the engineer, pointing to the manifold pressure-gauge. Dexter looked across, and at the same time felt the whole machine vibrating through the control column. He glanced out of the side window and saw the outboard nacelle shaking violently.

"Feather number one engine," he shouted. He saw Chuck's arm moving up to the feather-button, and watched the propeller as it slowed down and stopped. He corrected the yaw with a violent kick on the rudder-bar, and trimmed out the pressure on his right foot.

"Steer three-one-zero," the quiet voice from the ground continued.

Dexter heard Scott acknowledge and report that their number one engine was out. His voice was a little higher than usual, he thought.

"Roger, your engine out condition," continued the ground controller. "Steer zero-three-five . . . six miles from touch-down . . . commence your descent at six hundred feet a minute."

"Gear down, flap thirty . . . complete landing-check," shouted Dexter above the noise of the screen anti-ice hot air. He heaved the ship round on to the new heading.

"Steer zero-three-zero," whispered the voice in

Dexter's head-set. " On the glide path . . . four miles to touch-down."

Dexter looked up from his instruments momentarily.

Outside he could see nothing except an indistinct grey with horizontal streaks of white snow plunging towards them.

" Steer zero-three-two," continued the controller. " You're on the . . . stand by . . . stand by . . . climb ahead, repeat climb ahead on present heading . . . climb to two thousand feet. . . ."

" Set take-off power, gear up . . . flaps twenty," yelled Dexter. He corrected the yaw caused by the sudden surge of power, and pulled the machine into a climbing attitude.

" Visibility reduced to two hundred yards in blowing snow . . . cloud base indefinite," continued the controller. " Climb ahead to two thousand feet and rejoin the range-holding pattern."

" Flaps up," said Dexter as the machine increased its speed. It was suddenly very turbulent, and he fought the controls to maintain height on the three bellowing engines. They must be passing right over the field now, thought Dexter, and as the airspeed jerked up to the hundred and sixty knot mark he called for rated power. At last they reached two thousand feet and he reduced the power.

It was stifling hot inside the cockpit—despite the sub-zero temperature outside—and his hands were sticky with sweat. With a quick movement he wiped the palms of his hands on the thighs of his trousers. Outside he could see the motionless propeller, festooned with ice, plough-ing its way through the blinding greyness. It was still bumpy, and the ship groaned like an ancient man-of-war.

Above the background of noise Dexter was suddenly aware of a woman's voice sobbing. It was the woman of course. In the concentration of his approach and the over-shoot he had forgotten her completely. He turned round to see Mary standing behind the engineer.

" It's Mrs Pasquier ; she's getting a bit hysterical," she said. " She's having her pains again. The sooner we get her in proper medical care the better."

" It's not as if we haven't got enough on our plate already," replied Dexter with disgust, " Gander has just closed in on us."

" How long have we got to stay up here then?" asked Mary.

Dexter was interrupted by the voice of Gander Centre. Scott had changed frequency after their over-shoot, and had requested further weather information. Gander was still closed, and gave no promise of improvement for the next few hours. Stephenville was open, so he decided to divert there. Scott got a new clearance, and Dexter climbed the machine up to six thousand feet. The air was still rough, and Dexter sighed to himself, knowing that in fifty minutes he would have landed at Stephenville, and wouldn't have the responsibility of the expectant mother any more.

" Totem three-four-seven . . . message from company," Gander Centre crackled in his head-set.

" Roger, go ahead," replied Scott.

" Company advises . . . message from Harmon Field . . . no medical facilities available for six hours, stop. Facilities available at Moncton, also medical crew standing by at Gander, stop. Advise your intentions."

" Roger . . . stand by," said Scott, looking askance at Dexter.

Dexter swore under his breath. ' Do they think that I am God to make a snap decision like that?' he thought to himself.

" Let's look at that Moncton forecast again," he said. Scott passed over the weather sheet. It wasn't very good. Light snow showers, but above company limits, and no deterioration, he noted.

He called back to the navigator, " See if we can make Moncton and back to Stephenville on three engines at this altitude."

Mary had come up again and was standing behind the engineer.

" How long can the woman last, d'you think?" Dexter asked.

" It's hard to say, sir," she replied. " She's certainly got labour pains all right. She might carry on for hours like this—but it's pretty weakening. She said it's always been an easy delivery before."

" The main thing is to get her on the ground," said Dexter. " But they've got no facilities at Stephenville."

" Don't worry about my side of the job, sir," she continued. " We've got everything set up if things start moving. Oxygen, blankets, towels. And Anne is standing by in the galley with plenty of boiling water. We've even checked over the drill in the Emergencies book."

" Thanks, Mary," he said—thinking that her quiet factual voice was out of character with her young face, and the soft brown curl that had crept over her forehead.

The navigator nudged Mary, and she moved back to allow him to pass.

" It's O.K. for Moncton, sir," he said. " We can make Moncton and back to Stephenville plus fifteen minutes holding. It'll take an hour twenty-five to Moncton from overhead Stephenville."

"That's good," said Dexter. "O.K., Scott; tell Gander we'll continue to Moncton."

Thirty minutes later they were flying over the top of Stephenville. The only good field in the Maritimes—weatherwise, and no medical facilities. There were a few breaks in the cloud and the runways stood out sharply, the hard-packed snow bordered by dark markers.

"Say, Harmon Tower," called Dexter, "how come you've no medical personnel down there? I've got an expectant mother on board, and would have appreciated landing there."

Harmon Tower replied that an Air Force machine had come down in the Bay early that morning, and the medical team had gone out on rescue. They weren't expected back till after nightfall. All the crew were safe apparently—a few broken limbs but nothing serious.

"Well, I guess it's one of those things that makes aviation interesting!" said Dexter drily.

He eased the machine round on to the new heading towards Charlottetown, then looked out of the side window at the stationary propeller. He wondered if they could fix the anti-icer on the prop when he landed at Moncton. It would probably delay them. As a last resort he could have the prop cleaned down and smeared with Icex—that would be enough to get them off again. He could of course try to unfeather it now. It would cut down the time to Moncton—running on four motors. Still, with an unbalanced, iced-up prop it would probably vibrate so violently that it would wrench itself off the mounting—it might even smash onto the inboard prop—then he really would be in trouble. No, he couldn't contemplate it. If the winds had been lighter and he had been able to stick to schedule without all these set-backs he would have been on the ground at Montreal by now. Poor Margaret and the kids, he thought ; they've got a long time to wait yet.

" Estimate for Moncton is twenty-one fifty-four," said the navigator, breaking in on his thoughts.

" Thanks," said Dexter. " Keep a good check on our ground speed—and watch our fuel."

Ahead he could see that they were going to be on instruments again. The patchy sky over Stephenville and the Gulf was thickening up. It looked as if they would have a rough ride all the way to Moncton. He switched on the seat-belt sign and peered into the radar screen. Very quickly the ship was enveloped in cloud again. They plunged in and out of lighter and darker patches. It would be getting dark by the time they reached Moncton, practically twilight, he thought. Just about the worst light to land in, especially on instruments, with cloud and snow-covered ground merging into a meaningless nothing.

The radio compass needle on his instrument panel wavered, hesitated, and finally flopped round to the reciprocal heading.

" Check over Charlottetown, Scott," said Dexter, " and get our descent clearance from Moncton. I'll creep her down slowly to save fuel."

Dexter checked his watch with the instrument clock and wound it back five hours. Nine-thirty in the evening London time . . . four-thirty in the afternoon Eastern standard. Another fifteen minutes to Moncton.

" Moncton's weather is coming through, sir," said

Scott. "We're cleared to eighteen hundred feet at the range station."

Dexter pulled his head-set over his ears, ". . . wind from the north at fifteen knots gusting to twenty. Cloud base variable—three to four hundred overcast—visibility fifteen hundred yards—runway two-nine in use—hard-packed snow with two inches of soft snow on top—caution, snow-piles on either side of runway four feet high—braking action reported fair."

"Tell 'em I want to use runway zero-seven," said Dexter. "It'll be a cross wind on two-nine . . . tell 'em I'll do an ILS on two-nine and circle onto zero-seven."

Scott requested the alternative runway, but was told they could not use it. It had not been cleared after the snow-storm earlier that morning.

"Field approach check," said Dexter.

"You're cleared to land on runway two-nine. Check the outer marker," said Moncton Tower in Dexter's head-set.

He reduced power, and the flaps went out.

"My glide slope's not operating!" said Dexter. "How's yours, Scott?"

"Negative slope on mine," said Scott.

"Moncton Tower," said Dexter into his mike. "We've got no glide-slope indication on our sets—check your equipment."

"Roger, Totem," replied the Tower. "Our equipment was checked half an hour ago—was O.K. then. Stand by—I'll investigate."

"I'll hold in the range pattern," said Dexter. "Cloud base is below my minima without a glide slope."

Dexter uncoupled the auto-pilot and turned the machine into the oval holding pattern. He pulled the flaps in, and Chuck reduced the power to maximum three-engine endurance.

Above the engine noise, Dexter was aware that the woman's groans now had a sharper urgency. She had been moaning for the past half-hour or so, but he had tried to shut the sound out of his mind. He turned to see Mary standing behind the engineer's seat.

" Pretty soon now, I think," she said. " Could you press the call-bell, please, sir? I'd like Anne up here to help me."

" O.K., Mary," said Dexter quietly, and pressed the buzzer. " See if you can make the woman hold on a bit longer if possible. We're right over Moncton now—but we've got to hang around a bit—they've got a radio snag down there."

" I'll try," she said, and returned to her patient.

" Say, Moncton," called Dexter. " What's the position with that glide slope?"

" No news yet, sir," said the ground controller. " The radio engineer's out in the hut right now checking it over. I'll advise as soon as I get anything."

" What's the latest cloud base?" asked Dexter again.

" Still the same, three to four hundred variable," replied Moncton.

" This is my position," said Dexter gravely. " If you can push that cloud base up to five hundred feet, I'll have a go at landing without the glide slope. I'm on three engines, and I'm not going any lower in case of over-shoot. In five minutes' time, if you haven't fixed that glide slope, I'll have to divert to Stephenville ; I'm doing that on minimum fuel. Thirdly, I'd like you to bring the Doc up to the tower and have him stand by. Our woman passenger is getting pretty near birth, I think: we may need some advice."

"Roger, Totem three-four-seven," replied Moncton. "Your message understood. About the cloud base, it looks nearer three hundred feet from the Tower here . . . but I'll advise any improvement."

"Get me another weather sequence," said Dexter, turning to Scott. "Sydney or Charlottetown may have opened up, and we'll be able to hang around a bit longer if necessary."

"We've got one hour and thirty minutes' fuel left," said Chuck, "working on long-range cruise."

"O.K.," said Dexter. "I'll make a decision in a moment." He glanced up at the fuel-gauges—the main tanks looked uncomfortably low. "Is there any fuel left in those alternate tanks?" he asked.

"There might be a drain, sir," the engineer replied.

"Well, I'd like you to drain 'em completely. Take it one at a time, and run 'em off until the engine quits," said Dexter, "then run out number one main fuel tank."

"O.K., sir," replied Chuck, and he leaned over the pedestal and shifted the tank cocks.

Dexter continued to fly the machine round the two-minute oval holding pattern. By now it was quite dark. The cloud was lumpy and he was feeling terribly tired. Occasionally, flurries of snow swept across the windscreen. Outside, the motionless propeller, reflected icily in the wing flood-light, looked like some enormous cross in a ghostly churchyard.

"I've got the latest weather," said Scott, passing over the sheet. "No improvement anywhere except Gander."

"Well, that's just our luck," said Dexter, glancing over the list. "Gander's no good to us now, it's always the same with Gander. You get real close in and she closes up on you, and promises to stay closed. You decide to leave—and when you get too far away, she opens up again."

"Totem three-four-seven," Moncton Tower burst in on his headset. "We've found the fault in the glide slope. Snow shorted the aerial lead to the transmitter. The engineer says he can fix it in fifteen minutes."

"I'm right down on fuel now," replied Dexter. "I should divert to Stephenville, but if you can guarantee that the glide slope can be fixed, I'll continue to stand by here. Also I'd like a guarantee on the weather: is there any chance that you'll have a deterioration?"

"Totem three-four-seven." Moncton Tower sounded rattled. "The radio engineer says he can fix it, and the met. office aren't forecasting any deterioration."

"Roger, I'll advise," said Dexter quietly.

The easy way out would be to go straight back to Stephenville right now. He looked round and could see both Mary and Anne leaning over the expectant mother. No, that wasn't the answer. He should have held overhead Gander in the first place, but they had told him there would be no improvement.

"Moncton Tower!" Dexter made up his mind. "I'll remain here in the holding pattern until the glide slope is rectified."

"Roger, Totem three-four-seven," replied Moncton. "I'll advise you as soon as it's fixed."

So the die was cast. There was nothing he could do about it now; it was out of his hands. There was nowhere else he could go. Eventually he would have to come down and make an approach before the fuel ran out.

Down below, Dexter could imagine the engineer trying to fix the aerial: heavily clad, with thick gloves, probably with the light of a torch—the cold wind and biting snow tearing at his clothes.

"How's it going, Mary?" Dexter called back to the hostess.

She looked up. Over her face she was wearing an antiseptic mask. Seems efficient enought, thought Dexter.

"It's just started, sir. I think we can cope," she said briefly.

The minutes dragged by slowly. The fuel got lower. If they haven't got that glide slope fixed in twenty minutes I'll have to land without it, thought Dexter. He looked at the chart, and calculated the rate of descent. He'd have to break company regulations and descend below the prescribed minimum height. His imagination started to work. They would probably break cloud to find themselves too high ; he would cut the power and hurl the machine on to the runway, and in the high cross-wind he'd probably slew off it, crumpling props and engines into the snow-bank at the side.

"I could do with a cup of coffee," he said to Scott.

"So could I," replied the co-pilot.

"I don't think we can trouble the girls right now, though," said Dexter. "They're too busy. Say, Chuck ; do you think you could persuade our navigator to try and make some for us?"

"I'll try," he said—and leaned back to ask the navigator.

"My glide slope's coming in," said Scott suddenly.

Dexter looked at his own instrument, and saw the warning flag sliding out of sight.

"Totem three-four-seven . . . glide slope now serviceable," came the voice of Moncton Tower. "You're cleared for an ILS approach and landing on two-nine."

Dexter turned the machine round onto the approach path and lined up the miniature plane on the instrument with the hairpin needle. He called for the landing check. The wheels thumped down, and the three green lights came on. The glide slope needle started moving down, and he reduced the power. At just above two hundred feet Scott called out that the runway lights were ahead.

He looked up, and called for full flap. The threshold light swept underneath him, and he eased the control column back.

"Power off!" he called, and the machine settled gently on to the runway, and immediately started bucking over the icy patches.

"Reverse inboard!" he yelled, and the machine decelerated in the surge of engine noise. Soon the blowing snow from the reversed thrust obscured his vision in the landing-lights and obliterated the runway markers.

"Forward thrust!" he called, and threw the aileron control over to prevent the ship from sliding off the runway. The cross-wind was trying to push the huge tail round.

He touched the brakes gingerly, and brought the machine to a standstill. The snow fell gently upon the windscreen, and over to his left he could see the lights of the Terminal building.

"Totem three-four-seven. You're cleared to one-eighty and backtrack. Taxi to the Terminal," came Tower through his head-set. He heard Scott acknowledge, and turned the machine with the nose steering-wheel, opening the throttles a little to start the machine rolling again.

"Take it gently sir," said Anne across the engineer's shoulder, "we've got another passenger!"

"Good God!" said Dexter. He looked back to see Mary supporting a blanketed bundle on the navigator's table.

"It's a boy," Anne continued. "I guess we can add midwifery to our attributes in the Company's file back at Toronto now!"

Just then the navigator came stumbling through the door. "I've brought the coffee, sir," he said. "I'm afraid most of it's slopped in the saucer, though!"

Dexter smiled. "Give it to the girls," he said with a grin; "they need it more than us!"

Up ahead the terminal building was getting closer. He saw the lighted batons of the marshaller waving him in. A dark ambulance, its red roof-light winking, moved round in front of him. He stopped the engines. A ladder was wheeled up outside the crew door and a blast of cold air swept in as the door was opened.

It was nearly four hours later when they finally landed at Montreal. Mrs Pasquier and her son had been left behind in a hospital ward in Moncton.

The ground engineers had cleaned down the faulty prop, and had rectified it sufficiently for the two hours' flight to Montreal.

As Dexter left the machine and walked towards the new terminal building, he paused for a moment. He looked up at the totem-pole insignia on the huge tail reflected in the ramp light.

'Well, I won't be seeing you for another two weeks,' he thought, and turned, crunching across the packed snow towards the customs hall.

Margaret was waiting for him by the barrier. Diffused

music wafted away his tension, and the bright lights and hubbub of the passengers brought him back to earth.

" I've left the children in an hotel down town," she said. " We couldn't have gone today, the road to the cottage has been blocked with snow. It should be clear tomorrow."

" Have you been waiting long?" he asked.

" No ; the office told me you were going to be late. I thought you might be tired, so I booked two rooms. The children should be asleep in one of them by now. I said they could watch television until half-past nine. What held you up? Was it headwinds?"

" Yes, it was headwinds. And one or two other things," he replied. He would tell her the rest later, he thought. He *was* tired. Yes, he would tell her much later.

[' Maga ' May 1962.

6

A GLIMPSE OF THE STRATOSPHERE

Tony Smythe

It is half-past four on a dark rainy morning in late
September. From my position ten feet above the ground
in the cockpit of a Javelin night-fighter, I look out through
rain-beaded perspex on a dreary scene. All round in the
blackness of the airfield lights flicker, bright and wet, red
and green and yellow, while forward and left, stretching
away in giant perspective, are two lines of white lights.
Between them is a river of darkness, straight and flat,
fifty yards wide and two thousand yards long.

That is the runway.

The runway makes me vaguely uneasy. I have that
feeling of standing on a station platform when a non-stop
express is due. This is because, within a few minutes, I
will be racing down that runway, accelerating from rest
to a hundred miles an hour in ten seconds. To two
hundred in twenty seconds. To four hundred in forty.

I am shortly to take off on a high-level navigation
flight.

Like my navigator in the back cockpit, I am dressed,
or trussed rather, very fully and very securely with a
dozen nylon straps and cords, rubber wires and tubes. I

wear a light-grey flying-suit, and an orange inflatable life-jacket equipped with a miniature radio. My head is burdened with a helmet and earphones, a black rubber oxygen-mask with built-in microphone, and over all, a nylon fibre 'bone dome'—a crash-helmet—equipped with a dark visor and painted silver to reflect the intense sunlight of high altitude.

My seat is flat and not very comfortable, and, to an inquiring eye, very odd. It is mounted on rails leaning back and upwards, pointing skywards, and above my head there is a yellow-and-black striped rubber handle. The seat, however, is a marvellous life-saving device, an ejection-seat. It is my last means of escape if the vast complex machine I ride should irretrievably fail. Then, if I pull the black-and-yellow handle, I am fired in the seat up the rails, like a bullet from the doomed aircraft, and an automatic mechanism then releases me from the seat, operates my parachute, and leaves me nothing else to do until I reach earth. Thus the handle is a good one. Reach it blind, semi-conscious, suffocating, injured, it will work just the same.

But a pilot hasn't normally got time to think about bailing out once he's strapped into his aircraft. My eyes rove slowly round the familiar cockpit, from left to right, resting for a moment on each one of over a hundred switches, warning-lights and dials. A landlubber, when he looks into a jet cockpit, will often say, " But how can all these instruments mean anything to you at the speed you fly?" The answer is simple. It is a pattern the pilot is looking at, a pattern he has grown accustomed to. Should one instrument read too high, one warning-light come on, or one switch be forgotten, the pattern will have a different shape, and the error will be as noticeable as a missing paving-stone in Piccadilly.

When I have satisfied myself that all is prepared for start-up, I signal to the ground-crew below, and they acknowledge by waving a torch in a slow circular motion. I reach down to my right, and throw four switches linked together by a single bar. These are the starting electrics. An enormous current flows into fuel-pumps, inverters, heaters and gyroscopes. It is an electrical drain that would cripple the small aircraft battery in a few seconds, but before this can happen, I raise two red spring flaps, and press the two engine starter-buttons underneath. There is a giant hiss from the liquid-fuel starters, and a dozen instruments begin to flicker. This lasts for several seconds, as the starter-motors spin the two enormous turbojet engines ever faster. Then, just as the hiss ceases, the aircraft begins to vibrate to the tune of a dual-note, deep-throated burbling. The engines have lit up. Revolutions increase, oil-pressure rises, and jet-pipe temperatures soar—five, six, seven hundred degrees centigrade. I ease back the partly-open throttles and the burbling gives way to a fine scream, like a vacuum-cleaner going on in the next room. The two Sapphire engines are idling. Even now they have the power of three racing-cars, and boost the aircraft with a steady push against its hydraulically-locked brakes.

Outside in the darkness there is bustling activity as the ground-crew cover a few last jobs. While they are doing them, I check my flight instruments—the gyroscopic artificial horizon wobbles briefly before settling as still as a rock at sixty thousand r.p.m. I check a dozen fuel-indicators and cocks, heaters, flaps, and trim-settings, and lastly, most vital of all, the free, correct movement of the hydraulic-powered controls. In the mirror above my head—just like a car's—I watch the enormous tailplane slab move up and down as I pull and push the stick, watch it exert its ten-ton adjustments as accurately and smoothly as a pair of laboratory scales. I feel the oxygen flowing coldly over my cheeks, and I take a pull on my harness-straps, although they are tight enough already.

Fifty seconds have passed.

I press the radio transmit button. " 695, taxi and take-off."

The answer is immediate. " 695, you're clear to line up and take off. Surface wind 290 degrees, 20 knots. Runway wet."

" All right, Lawrie?" I ask my navigator.

" Fine, Tony. Whenever you like," he answers, already absorbed in his equipment.

I wave the ground-crew clear, and edge open the throttles. The engines accelerate slowly at first, then spin up in a leap. I check them at a medium-power setting, release the brakes and the aircraft rolls, as big and cumbersome as a ship, onto the runway. I turn to the left with short stabs of the brakes, until I point the nose carefully at the horizon junction of the two lines of lights. Then I sweep the throttles open. There is a short, twin screech that leaps beyond the range of human hearing, and a giant suppressed roar. As the aircraft begins to roll, I have time for a quick glance at the engine r.p.m. indicators and jet-pipe temperatures (within limits, O.K.) before looking up to concentrate on the take-off. There is a feeling of enormous acceleration, the biggest of all pushes in the back. The runway lights racing silently by become two blurred streaks of light. The nosewheel lifts, and I hold it at a well-judged two feet. The airspeed comes up like the second hand of a watch, and at 145 knots I apply a light back-pressure on the stick. The light, super-cushioned jolts cease ; we are airborne. A few moments ago I was directing a heavy, cumbersome, wheeled machine. Now it is alive, delicate, flying. I brake the free-spinning wheels, and select undercarriage up. And still that relentless push in the back, now quickly threatening the undercarriage limiting speed of 220 knots. But three thuds, three indicator lights out, and the wheels are safely tucked in the wings. And all the time the short light movements of the controls with my hands, and the scanning of the blind-flying instruments with my eyes, tell me that the dark ground below is falling away, at the correct rate, in the correct direction.

We gain height slowly at first, accelerating almost level with the earth. I notice a few lights sweeping by underneath, but the country is asleep. At 450 knots I point the nose up at the black clouds, and, as though summoned, they fall at us. In them, like cloud on a mountain. The instruments in front of me, illuminated by concealed red and ultra-violet lights, register correctly, soothingly. The aircraft bumps slightly, the only complaint in its task of hurtling through cloud at five hundred miles an hour on a dark night. But suddenly we are through, and above. The lumpy floor of cloud, an ocean of it in the white moonlight, just drops away. Of all the exulting moments of flying, surely this is the greatest.

Above, a clean hard moon and a fabulous dome of stars beckon. I aim the nose even higher, and the altimeter goes spinning wild. Soon we are as high as Mont Blanc, and, lending yet more power to the engines in the thinning air, I select reheat. This is a system of feeding extra fuel into the jet pipes, and has the same effect as supercharging on a piston engine. There are two thumps, and power is restored like a gear. Now we rival the Andean peaks ; now we surpass them, and demolish Himalayan giants one by one. At thirty thousand feet we are higher than Mount Everest, higher than any point on earth. We enter the cold, silent stratosphere, where the temperature, having dropped to a merciless hundred degrees of frost, can shrink no further. The air is so thin that it can support no life, and human consciousness, without oxygen and a pressurised cabin, would be lost in a few seconds. Terrible winds of over a hundred miles an hour sweep this upper void, but a jet, flying close to the speed of sound, is scarcely deflected.

At forty thousand feet, pressure has fallen to 200 millibars, a fifth of that at sea level, and the thin air hardly supports the Javelin. She rides sluggishly but smoothly in the dark, her engines a mere whisper outside the warmth of the heated cabin. Outside the canopy, the air sweeps past ; and above and around, and even below to the horizon, is a glittering, powdered wealth of stars. To an astronomer, this intense clarity of space would be a pure and lovely gift ; my navigator and I can only afford a glance before our work begins.

We set out for a position far over the North Sea, decided by a pencilled cross on my navigator's chart. For the exercise to be successful we must fly so as to reach the position within seconds of the time previously calculated. Then, turning north, we will head for another turning-point, before returning to base.

Many of the calculations were worked out by my navigator before we took off. In the Squadron briefing-room there is a placard which baldly states that time on the ground is free, but that, in an emergency in the air,

seconds are beyond price. My navigator's log and chart
are covered with small pieces of information—the wind
strength and direction at all heights, which airfields are
open at this time of night, their exact positions, and how
much fuel we must have to reach any of them from any
point on our route.

He works ceaselessly at his task of directing the Javelin
along the track on his chart, obedient to the hands of his
watch. We talk little. In the mirror I can just see him
moving behind the mass of equipment separating us, now
taking a radar fix and plotting it, now looking down at
some instrument, or helping, with a judicious tap, another
which is not working too well.

My own job, once I have settled the aircraft at cruising
altitude and speed, is, for the moment, negative. Rather
like an engineer left on his own in a machine-shop, I
supervise rather than work. But the comparison stops
there. The machine-shop is massively built, bedded in
concrete, and equipped with master-power-switches and
emergency doors. The engineer can cut off the power to
a faulty machine and, if necessary, beat a retreat. My
own responsibilities are much greater. The Javelin's
engines, apart from their first function of thrusting us
forward high over the cold North Sea, are required to
drive the flying-instruments, the hydraulic-power controls, cabin pressure, radios—in fact, everything. Our
exits, the ejection seats, are rapid indeed, but they lead,
not into a yard or street, but into an icy sea, where a
rubber dinghy, a hundred miles from shore, is poor
protection against the rigours of an autumn night. And
besides, the Javelin costs the taxpayer a lot of money,
probably nearly half a million pounds.

My supervision is too alert for me to relax, even though

there is nothing to do at the moment. My eyes follow a ten-second route that never varies, and is repeated minute after minute. Outside the cockpit. Left. Front. Right. And above. You have very little time to see and avoid another aircraft on a collision-course at high altitude. Then inside the cockpit, at the instruments—a lingering, swinging glance. Outside. Left. Front. Right. . . .

In addition to my own eyes, the navigator works an electric one of greater efficiency and power. This is the search-radar. A beam of electrons sweeps the sky, probing for that tiny speck of metal in the boundless night that might spell disaster with a Capital D. A ' bogy ' on a head-on collision-course closes very quickly —at perhaps nearly twice the speed of sound, or a mile every three seconds. While visual range is perhaps ten miles, human reaction time and aircraft inertia reduce the safety margin to a few short seconds. Collision is a flying-man's secret fear. It eats into his subconscious. And if reason tells him that the sky is vast, fear and experience warn him that it is never big enough.

The minutes creep by. The fuel, drawn from sealed tanks, pumped and pressurised, filtered and metered, is being burned at white heat at hundreds of gallons an hour. In the cockpit, on the gauges, it dwindles imperceptibly, mathematically. In response, eighteen tons of Javelin sweep on with the steadiness and momentum of a ship, and, eight miles down, the moon shines in an open patch of water like burnished steel.

Then we reach the second turning-point, somewhere off the Yorkshire coast, and head for home.

Soon we are over the land again. Behind me, somewhere beyond Norway, the dawn is coming in, a delicate riot of red and green and yellow. The Aurora Borealis, a ragged fringe, a quivering curtain of light over the North Pole, is fading. Ahead, in the south and west, England is dark and flat and asleep. The moon sparkles prettily on the frost-patches on the canopy, but I'm tired and ready for bed. I yawn awkwardly into my oxygen-mask, shift slowly in my straps.

We fly down through Yorkshire and Lincolnshire. And suddenly the sun appears on the rim of the world, a bright yellow disc, spreading neither life nor warmth in the pitiless cold of the upper air. It lights up the windscreen-arch with a bold, theatrical colour, and pushes the night away, west, into the Atlantic.

At last it is time to descend. I close the engines, and allow the speed to fall before starting the long glide. Soon the hard cold wonders of the stratosphere are gone. The air thickens, and the airspeed rises. Suddenly the cockpit darkens again. In the east the sun is vanishing, an uncanny dawn in reverse as the plain dark earth rises slowly. The clouds have disappeared, and soon we are flying level at a thousand feet over the Cambridgeshire fields.

We fly downwind to the brightly-lit runway.

" 695, downwind, landing," I call to the yawning controller in the control-tower below.

" 695, you're clear to Finals," he answers methodically.

Wheels down. A rumbling noise meets my listening ear as the undercarriage unfolds, breaking the smooth contour of the delta wing under-surfaces. The legs lock in position with three satisfying jolts.

Flaps down, brake pressure sufficient. Fuel? Enough for another fifteen minutes' flying. We are 'fat'.

As I turn to land, the runway lights tilt, and then wander towards us. Height and speed shrink, and out of the corner of my eye I see dark fields and woods and farms going past. I cut the engines as the runway lights suddenly come at a run, and lower the great bird between them. A moment of quiet, a few light jolts, a rumbling nose-wheel, a long-drawn slowing with the brakes, and that's it.

I turn off the runway, open the hood, and feel the air like warm milk on my face. Soon the engines are spinning down, the ground-crew are crawling round the aircraft, and I am stretching and scratching in the keen dawn wind outside the hangar.

My navigator joins me, and we walk slowly across the tarmac towards the offices. Behind us the Javelin stands, a big awkward silhouette in the lightening sky. The second dawn.

We go into the office, and I take the aircraft's servicing log-book from the rack without waking the duty corporal. I find my pen and write a single word on the page.

'Satisfactory.'

[' Maga ' January 1961.

7

HOW GOES IT?
M. D. L.

We carried our bags up the steps of our hotel, then stopped to watch a bundle gliding down the ice-bound street. It drew closer, to resolve itself into a middle-aged woman wrapped in a coat of not-very-good fur. She could have passed for an English suburban housewife, one who had reached the point at which the once dependent children had taken to activities over which she had no control, and acquired interests which the cares of housekeeping had long ago driven out of her head. Here was a figure we all knew and associated with the comfortable, secure and unexciting life of our home towns ; a figure that was almost right, but not quite, because instead of padding down the street, she was standing on six-foot-long runners attached to the legs of a chair, her shopping-bag on the seat, gloved hands grasping the back and propelling her vehicle by occasional dignified thrusts with her right leg.

Apart from her the view up the main street might have been of any one of a number of small English towns in winter. There were the same types of shop—grocers and electricians, shoemakers and watchmakers, cafés, cinema and even a florist, with plate-glass windows, strip lighting and electrical signs. But there were differences. An illuminated clock-face showed that it was early afternoon, yet the thin twilight was outshone by festoons of light-bulbs strung across the street; a snow-covered mountainous island loomed in the background, its towering ruggedness as distinctively Norwegian as the parchment Christmas-star lampshades glowing in the windows of the private houses, or the giant Christmas-tree that twinkled from the highest point of the town.

The sight of the rapidly waning light reminded us that there was work to be done and we hurried to stow our bags in the spotless little hotel bedrooms with their scalding radiators. We flung on our parkas again and were soon on our way back to the airfield in a taxi, glad of its heater as we crossed the exposed causeway out of the town; for wisps of dry snow were being swept by the biting wind that flowed down from the mountains to the East.

In the control-tower the Canberra crew was working on plans for the afternoon flight. The three of them, all squadron leaders, made up a full load for the aircraft; for the bomb bay, where the 'payload' would normally have been, was occupied by the long black cylinder of an extra fuel tank to allow them to range more widely over the northern wastes, sharpening their skill on the special problems that confront the airman who will cross the top of the world.

Tom was the reason for the flight. Although always a navigator by trade, he had been diverted for the previous few years into the administrative side of an overseas headquarters. There his attempts to keep a building-programme in step with the shifts of higher policy had very nearly carried him past a point of no return to modern flying, which had been developing at a terrific rate in his absence. Fortunately his efforts were rewarded with an advanced flying course to put him once more into the front rank of practical navigators. He had proved that he was not too old a dog to learn new tricks, and now he was about to put his competence and courage as a jet navigator to the test, in the most navigationally barren area in the northern hemisphere.

His co-navigator, Geoffrey, was on the staff of the school, no novice at this business, and sustained by having made similar flights before. He could calculate with the same precision in the air as on the ground, and produce a reasoned course of action while the aircraft rushed through the night at 500 miles an hour, gulping down the fuel at the rate of a good bathful every ten minutes.

The pilot also was a member of the staff, but he was flying this route for the first time. Peter's previous experience as a jet flying instructor had confronted him with many emergencies, mostly created by his pilot students ; like the impetuous one who jabbed open the throttles at high altitude, dowsing the flame, and left him to glide to a lower altitude nursing the batteries and hoping that the relighting arrangements were really efficient. He had emerged from these and other incidents with confidence and almost mystical faith that he was destined to survive all the hazards his profession put in his way.

The three of them had just completed their plans. They could see that the aim they had set themselves, the attainment of that point where noon and midnight meet, the North Pole, was just within their reach if they used up a good deal of the ' fat ', or fuel reserve normally carried by jet pilots against the delays and diversions imposed by bad weather. Even at home jet pilots did not run themselves as short as these three now proposed to do, despite the fact that England was dotted with airfields. Here, within the Arctic Circle, their homecoming would be confined to one solitary mountain-infested strip on the edge of a fjord. Yet they did not view the journey they were to make as an act of desperate bravado. They believed in the product of their country's engineering genius, and they knew that theory by itself was not enough ; it had to be put to the test.

At any rate all this had been argued out long before ; the clock was telling them that if they were to take off at the time planned they ought to leave the superheated control-tower and go to the aeroplane.

The Canberra had already been towed from the heated hangar where the ground-crews and the electronics had been at their best in a dry temperature of 65°. Ice had been chipped from the rails on which the doors slid, and discreet nudges with the rear wheel of a tractor had been used to coax the doors open. Now a tanker emblazoned with a familiar name was topping up the aeroplane on the readiness platform near the beginning of the runway. Half a gale whipped the snow into racing, snaking lines about the feet of the attendant airmen, who withdrew into their quilted parkas with their hoods up against the earbiting 25° of frost. Beyond the low rocky hills at the edge of the airfield the fjord advertised its presence by a show of 'sea smoke' rising from the relatively warm waters and forming a thin line of cloud. Beyond that again the mountains seemed, in spite of their covering of snow, black against the brightness of the southern sky.

The crew piled their kit into the American waggon, with its humming heater. In went the navigators' brief-cases, crammed with charts, astronomical tables, reference books of radio frequencies and navigation aids over half the world ; in went the pilots' handbook with its pictures of airfields, some in such totally improbable places that the pilot making a bad-weather let-down over the sea had to be as wary as the sailor is of the towering uncharted icebergs, but without the sailor's ability to go astern or stop and think when in doubt. In went the crash-helmets, and the life-jackets still faithfully called Mae Wests in spite of the popularity of more recent priestesses of pneumatic bliss. On top of the baggage went the men themselves, wrapped warmly against the cold of the stratosphere which they knew would prevail over the warmth tapped from the Canberra's engines. Then the cheerful Nor-wegian driver slammed the door and took the wheel, to bowl confidently along the treacherous surface of the perimeter at a good forty miles an hour.

At the west end of the single long runway they passed over a track running between the rocky approaches on the seaward side and the gleaming runway itself. As the waggon drew to a halt the party saw with relief that the trunk-pipe from an aircraft heater ran through the door into the cockpit, so that they could at least hope to start in warm surroundings. Reluctantly they climbed out to the exposed tarmac, where the wind buffeted them, snatching at the hoods of their parkas until they had to turn their faces downwind and move with a crablike walk that made them look, in their shapeless clothes, as unlike men as any two-legged creatures had ever been.

Tom was to ride in the most inaccessible position in

the Canberra, so he climbed in first and crawled down the narrow alleyway, halting every few inches to unhitch some part of his harness. At last he got to the seat next to the one-foot-square pane of double glass which, when not covered with ice and frost, would provide him with his view of the outside world for some seven hours. With a gasp of relief he pulled up his bulging navigation bag and started to organise himself while a fumbling and cursing in the alleyway told him that Geoffrey was on his way in. Geoffrey was fulminating not so much at the designer of the torture chamber he was entering, as at the many lesser men whose brain-waves and after-thoughts, each one excellent in itself, seemed never to have been arranged and disciplined. At easier times he had often reflected that this was not the kind of work that could be done by committees. " What this problem needs," he had once said in a voluble moment in the officers' mess bar, " is a single individual with practical experience in a modern aircrew, the engineer's down-to-earth knowledge of how materials behave and of ways of doing things in metal and plastics, and above all the artist's passionate interest in creating a balanced whole out of a mass of unrelated and antagonistic parts." But such men are not found nowadays or at any rate life is not organised to encourage them to exercise their talents, and he had been shouted down for being pretentious and impractical.

By now Peter had climbed into his seat in the front, and the airframe mechanic was helping him to do up the parachute straps. The bright young Yorkshireman, who had made his way from an industrial city to this improbable spot in twelve months of national service, welcomed the opportunity to get out of the biting wind he had been enduring since the aircraft had been dragged from the hangar nearly an hour before. After a few minutes everyone was strapped in and connected up and the door could be closed and sealed. For those outside this introduced a particularly uncomfortable period of waiting in the cold with nothing to do. Inside the aircraft the checks were being carried out in quite a different atmosphere, each member of the crew being involved in following the check-list and confirming his checks to the captain. By the time they came to the legend 'Start Engines' the ground-crew were practically rooted to the concrete with cold, and it took the loud detonation of the starter cartridge in the No. 1 engine to wake them up. In spite of the temperature the jet engines could be run up to high power as soon as they had started, so Peter waved the chocks away at once and taxied forward, testing his brakes after a few yards to make sure that he had control on the slippery surface.

As he turned on to the short length of track leading to the runway he was glad that he had not far to go, because the high wind was getting at his controls from behind—a direction for which they were not balanced—and was making the rudder-bar and the 'spectacles' of the control-column lash about alarmingly, in spite of his using the full strength of leg and arm to keep them still. Fortunately the flying-control officer in the tower gave him permission for an immediate take-off, and he was able to relax as he turned into wind. He looked up the runway and was grateful for enough twilight to see the mountains in his path, then he made a quick movement of the controls to check that they were free, confirmed that the navigators were ready, and opened the throttles. It took a few seconds for the heavy turbines and compressors of the engines to pick up speed, and he watched the needles of the tachometers and the jet-pipe temperature-gauges to see that the acceleration went as it should. When he was satisfied that he was getting his power he let the brakes off and the heavy aircraft moved smoothly ahead.

After a run of about a mile he eased the Canberra off the ground and settled down to the next stage, the acceleration by a further 250 miles an hour to allow the engines to develop their greatest efficiency for the climb. During this time the aeroplane had to stay low, and Peter could get his last glimpses of the familiar details of the world from a fairly conventional viewpoint. As they charged on over the next two miles towards a hamlet in his path he seemed to have full leisure to take in the whole scene, the distinctive spire of the Lutheran church set on a hillock among stunted trees, the neat wooden houses, the tracks through the snow from a detached farmhouse, and the embyro snowdrifts building up against the drift fences along the main road. Then it was over and he was climbing at a steep angle, turning northwards towards the darkening sky and the far-distant Pole.

In less than ten minutes the snow on the great craggy barrier of the Lofoten Islands glimmered far below in the dusk ; then there was nothing underneath but the darkness covering the northern ocean.

The loneliness and immensity of the dark space outside began to have their effect. The navigator is mentally very much within his aircraft, busy with calculations or with some radio or radar mechanism whose dials and cathode-ray tubes have to be interrogated for the information he needs: the pilot often has the leisure and the opportunity to project his thoughts into the world outside, but when bad weather or darkness draws his horizons in he becomes more keenly aware of the activities of those in the back. So it was that Peter now listened more attentively to the technicalities being exchanged in unimpassioned professional tones between Geoffrey and Tom. The Canberra was reaching the top of the climb into the stratosphere where it was to cruise, profiting by the low resistance of the thin air, and the navigators were preparing to start their first series of sextant shots of the stars. The periscope of the sextant had been thrust up in the pressure lock, the electrically-heated object-glass was working overtime to keep clear of frost in the 500 miles an hour blast, and Geoffrey had been forced to free the swivelling action from clogging ice with heavier blows than he liked to direct at a delicate scientific instrument.

As the moment for the first fix approached, Tom, who was at the plotting-table and concentrating on the second hand of his watch, started his count-down—

"Thirty seconds to go! Ten, nine, eight. . . ."

Peter's family had been avid followers of the 'Journey into Space' broadcasts, and he had often tried to work out why a 'count-down' was needed for the launching of a spaceship—apart from the purely dramatic trick to build up tension. Momentarily he felt rather foolish to be involved in a count-down himself, but then he remembered that the accuracy of the sight would depend on how closely he could reproduce the conditions of speed and 'heading' for which it was calculated ; at the speed he was making it was not enough to follow his first flying-instructor's advice: "Leave her alone, boy! She can do it far better than you can." Now he must detect the slightest natural oscillations and instabilities, foresee them and oppose them. The count-down gave him a chance to prepare to concentrate hardest just for that space of time that would bring the most accurate result.

As he relaxed after the shot Peter became aware of a glow of light ahead. Looking up he saw a faint luminous cloud above, and for a moment thought that it was a patch of cirrus, until he remembered that there are no clouds in the stratosphere, and that any cirrus there might be would lie beneath him. Slowly the light strengthened and seemed to be taking on a more definite form—it was the aurora, and it was livening up for him.

He remembered that he had looked up some cold facts about the aurora before he left England. He knew that he was approaching the zone over which the most frequent displays occurred, and that the lower edge of the light would be some sixty miles above the surface of the earth. What he was not prepared for was the living thing there above him moving and brightening, sometimes showing distinct rays like a distant searchlight barrage, at other moments hinting at changing shades of green and red.

He was recalled to his task as the navigators steadied him for another set of sextant readings, and rejoined the team in spirit as he concentrated on the instruments. The needle of the machmeter magnified slight changes in speed until a single knot weighed on his conscience, while a wing-tip tank that was feeding too slowly pulled steadily on the control-column and tried to throw him off level. Geoffrey on his part was making final adjustments when he let out an exclamation of annoyance. The aurora, being a transitory and unfamiliar hazard, had not entered into the detailed calculations with which the navigators had prepared for the flight. It revenged itself and compelled attention by blanking out the view of the stars selected for navigation.

Before long, however, they drew up to the place where the aurora, now a curtain of vertical rays, was directly overhead. The effect of passing under this colossal gateway, which stretched away east and west as far as Peter could see, might have been to impress the crew with the awe of entering a mysterious sanctum. Of course they were reminded by it that a stage of the flight had been passed and that they were visibly farther from home, but as the glow passed out of sight astern they became aware of a sense of anticlimax. At night, when the clouds and the surface of the earth are hidden in the pitchy void beneath, all the world is the same to the eyes of the Canberra crew ; the 'night of tropical splendour' owes its wonder to the qualities of the lower atmosphere, just as the pin-point clarity of the view from a polar station on a still night is the gift of a shallow, dust-free atmosphere. High above all the 'make-up' that gives character to the sky the airman's reactions to the area he is crossing will often lie at the end of a train of calculation—

> 'So many knots for so many minutes in this direction puts us over X. I remember Tomkins telling me about the trappers who live there.'

> or

> 'With Polaris up there on the edge of the canopy we must be getting near 80° North—there's not much land north of here.'

On a dark night only the aurora gives a crew in the stratosphere that immediate, unthinking, sensual appreciation of place and climate. Now Peter and Tom and

Geoffrey had passed beyond it to a sky as commonplace as that over their base in East Anglia.

After a few minutes cruising on instruments, Peter thought of the next feature he hoped to see and asked Tom the time to Isfjord in Spitsbergen. The powerful lights of the mining settlements there would show even through a covering of cloud. Tom seized a pair of dividers and a slide-rule and rapidly computed the estimated time of arrival at Isfjord, then pushed the instruments aside and returned to his astro calculations. The hands of his watch seemed to be spinning round to the time when his next sight would be due.

Once again the crew concentrated on the routine of complicated drills, until the sextant shutter had closed for the last time and the last set of figures had been read as the averaging mechanism came to a halt. By then they were a hundred miles closer to Isfjord. When Peter relaxed from his instruments and looked out ahead he could see a glimmer on the ground, and then more patches of light showed up, irregularly scattered across his path. He repeated the names, Longyearbyen, Barentsberg, Pyramiden, Grumantbyen, and as their lights became more definite he felt refreshed and reassured, almost as if he had been nearing the cities flanking his home base. There was little logic in this sensation ; for there were barely 4000 souls among those lights, hedged in by sharp-edged mountains and ice-filled fjords. Besides, more than half of them were Russians, who would have greeted the descent of a British bomber and its crew with anything but friendly interest. All the same, reason is not man's strong point when he sees signs of human occupation in the barren places of the world, and Peter, sealed up *incommunicado* in an aluminium box ten miles above an inaccessible Arctic settlement, was warmed by the comradeship it radiated.

All too soon the lights disappeared beneath the wings, and once more the strange glow of the luminous instrument dials dominated the view. Peter's attention switched again to the occasional exchange of technicalities between the navigators, which assured him that all was going well in their world, where comfort of mind was represented by an orderly procession of crosses marching across the chart in the pool of orange light from an Anglepoise lamp. He looked at the fuel gauges and at his watch, and began to steady the aircraft for the next sextant shots, which Tom introduced by passing the figures for Geoffrey to set up on the dials of the instrument.

When the shots were over Tom completed his quick computation of the position and set to applying this to the ' How Goes It ' graph. This unassuming sheet of paper was the ultimate arbiter of the flight ; for when you go to the maximum radius of action it is not good enough to hope that everything will follow the plan, and blithely fly on to the turning-point at the half-way mark. Geoffrey knew that an adverse wind or a slight increase in fuel consumption would force them to turn early, so he was relieved to see that his entry of pounds-of-fuel-left against miles-covered fell on the predicted line. Cheerfully he reported: " On the line " ; and Peter and Tom knew that they were still well placed to reach the Pole.

Instinctively Peter looked out ahead. Craning to see past a patch of frost in the sandwich of his plastic canopy, he became aware of a strange luminosity on the thin clouds far below as the rising moon was reflected from the endless ice and snow of the Arctic Ocean. The menace of that ' ice-blink ' seemed more real as the cold of the stratosphere gradually beat the aircraft's heating system and announced its victory by a thickening crust of frost on the cockpit coaming.

Tom and Geoffrey were also beginning to notice the cold. They were used to working with exposed fingers, a familiar occupational hazard for navigators, who could not afford to have the speed and accuracy of their work degraded by bulky gloves ; what did seem to be discomfort beyond the call of duty was the cold that struck up from the metal floor through the rubber soles of the boots of the immersion suits. Tom, in particular, suffered from a blast of air playing on his kidneys ; this was meant to be hot, but in competing with the outside temperature of 100° of frost it had long since ceased to be even tepid and merely contributed to the general chill. The roof was encrusted with frost from their breath, and the glitter of it in the light reflected from the chart seemed to add to the wintry atmosphere, although they knew that it was harmless enough like that, and would only become a real nuisance at the end of the flight, when it would drip great smudges on the chart and log during the descent to warmer layers.

Tom felt the contrast with the centrally-heated hotel room he had left so few hours ago and his spirits sank ; and this was where Geoffrey's matter-of-fact approach began to come in. Through his morbid ponderings Tom heard the instructor ' making a teaching point ' in his dry, professional tones just as if they had been in a classroom or, at the worst, in one of the grooves they had worn in the sky on a standard cross-country route over Britain. He could have laughed at the introduction of the instructor-student relationship out there where every channel of their wireless-receiver was silent, and each member of the crew depended so much on the other two, but the control and confidence in Geoffrey's manner stifled his mirth with admiration.

The moon was rising fast, and through a clearing in the clouds below Peter could trace dimly the contours of the ice hummocks, endlessly repeated as far as he could see. His watch told him that there was just half an hour to go to the Pole, and the thought that nothing was now likely to force him to turn short of his goal raised his spirits to a point at which the menace of the ice failed to impress him. In truth the excitement he felt was based on nothing more than his faith in the professional qualities of Geoffrey and Tom. When they said they were at 90° North he would turn back; but he would not really be sure that this was correct until afterwards, when, leaning over the chart-table under the fluorescent lights in the Norwegian Air Force briefing-room, he could see the neat crosses marking successive positions, and perhaps be bold enough to check the figures on the log-sheet—so neatly entered up that it was hard to believe that the pencil had been gripped in mittened hands resting on an ice-cold chart-table with a back-drop of frost-encrusted instruments.

As he scanned the horizon in a mood of growing exhilaration, Peter became aware that there was something in view apart from the moon and the ice and the clouds. A vapoury but distinct wall of flame was rising out of the distant floes—or so it seemed. For a moment he was perplexed, but then he remembered the northern lights he had passed under some two hours before; these had the same structure and must surely be the same, but their point of origin seemed strange. He knew that the aurora had been measured many times and found to begin some 300,000 feet above the surface, yet the base of these lights was below him as seen from a mere 46,000 feet. Had he, as one of the first men to observe these parts from such a height, made some new discovery? He thought of his long-discarded ambition to be a scientist, a member of the Royal Society acclaimed for his contributions in some apparently purposeless study ; then the keen wind of common sense blew such thoughts away. The lights he saw *were* the northern lights, but they were the display on the other side of the world, over towards the North Siberian shore. Because of their distance their lower edge was hidden by the curvature of the earth, so that they seemed to spring out of the ice-bound horizon.

By now the navigators were ready for the most vital fix of all, and as they set up the sextant they warned Peter to steady up for the series of sights. In the cramped space each one of them could only cover a limited field of view, so that in order to get a ' good cut ' of the position lines they had to take turns with the instrument, undoing their safety-straps and twisting awkwardly to do so. It was Geoffrey's task to take the second pair of observations, and as each one came up Tom quickly plotted it on the chart. The last entry was no sooner made than Tom called Geoffrey over. They had evidently been making a better speed than originally calculated and were, by the evidence of the fix, just past their destination. Tom quickly told Peter to go into the long fifteen-miles turn needed to reverse their direction.

At the great height and speed it was not easy for Peter to fly the Canberra round the turn without gaining or losing height, but he concentrated on responding quickly but lightly to the slight indications of his altimeter and his gyro horizon, so as to do a turn worthy of the stage of the flight they had reached.

As they settled down on the homeward heading the navigators once more busied themselves with the sextant; the long turn was likely to have disorganised the gyro compass, and they wanted to check their course as quickly as possible in case they were burning up precious pounds of fuel going in the wrong direction. To check the heading they had set up the sextant so that its eye, protruding into the icy blast of the attenuated air on the outside of the pressure compartment, was looking in the supposed direction of a selected star. The field of view was too narrow to allow much room for error, and to pick up the wrong star and apply the right one's calculations to it could be inconvenient or even disastrous.

When Geoffrey peered into the instrument Peter was disconcerted to hear that all was not going well. The expected star, identified by its brilliance and by the positions of its immediate neighbours, had not turned up. The navigators went back over their arithmetic while Peter continued to steer the heading he had been given, but now looking at it suspiciously and calculating despondently that even if they were only 5° out for the next half-hour they would then be twenty miles off track. However, there was nothing he could do about it except to cut down the number of variables by steering as accurately as possible. He remembered his first reaction to getting lost in the air when he was flying a cross-country at his training-school; in a moment of panic he had attempted to stop the headlong (as it seemed to him then) progress of the old biplane by circling and trying to match some feature on the ground with the shapes on his map. This finally demolished his feeble sense of direction and the flight ended with a landing in a field far from home. He still remembered the pleasure of being treated as a hero by the family in the big house next to the field, and the growth of his unease as the time drew near for his instructor to land and take him back. No pupil who gets lost in fine weather is a hero to his instructor.

Now there were no fields and no big houses. If he went down out of fuel there would be no instructor to fly out and pick him up. The only things that were the same were the ' butterflies in the tummy ' and the dryness in the throat as he was assailed by a fear of trouble not too far ahead. But he need not have worried ; for Geoffrey was equal to the emergency and in a few minutes had selected a bright and unambiguous star, made the new calculations and set up his instruments for the new heading check. Once more the team settled down to the careful flying and sighting that would produce the information they required. There was a period of silence while Tom worked out the figures he had been given, then he said—

" No wonder we couldn't find our star. The gyro compass drifted eight degrees during that turn."

Now it was possible to start the routine again, but they wanted more assurance of position than the unaided sextant could give. The receiver of the radio compass, which could indicate the direction from which a wireless signal was being transmitted, was turned on. As he waited for it to warm up Geoffrey looked at the almost unbelievably remote position of the station he hoped to hear, marked by a conventional sign on his chart. He had once landed at an Arctic settlement, so it was easy for him to visualise the situation down there, where a small party of men living in huts huddled in the snow had, a few hours before, received a message to turn on their beacon. In their oasis of warmth and light in the continuous dark of the polar night they had thrown a switch, so that now their settlement was marked by the rays of a kind of invisible lighthouse to which he tuned his set. First he selected the wavelength, just as he might have done on his wireless at home, then he turned up the volume and listened to the steady note that came through. After a minute two letters were slowly and distinctly transmitted in morse. They matched those marked against the lonely spot on his chart and he knew that he had made his contact. A turn of the selector switch threw in the automatic directional aerial and he looked for the uncanny swing of the radio compass needle which should follow the aerial as it peers and searches and finally settles to point at the transmitting-station. When it has done this and has 'locked on' to the beacon, inching round as the station passes from abeam to the quarter and then more gradually astern, it gives all the comfort to an uncertain crew of a hand stretched out in the dark, to grip and steer and reassure. But now it did not budge.

In the moment of disappointment that followed Geoffrey realised how cold he was. His feet were numb, and the chilling contact of his clothes made him tuck in his back and sit bolt upright like a Victorian governess. His fingers, protruding from the woollen mittens that allowed him to manipulate switches and computors and use his sharp-pointed pencil with precision, were pinched bluey white ; the roof of the cabin and the faces of the instruments were frosted like the pipes of a refrigerator with the moisture from his and Tom's breath. But his mood only lasted a few seconds, no more than a glimpse of the normal, fearful groundling. Leaving his frost-bound radio compass he turned to help Tom with his preparations for the coming sight, which now had so much more importance than it seemed to have a minute before —nine miles back in the trackless night.

The sight ran through until, in twelve minutes, they were almost relieved to see that they were well off track in a direction that made sense when taking into account the compass drift after their homeward turn. They settled into the routine again and relaxed as far as the cold would allow. Peter, having checked his oxygen and his engine instruments, looked back over his shoulder to the setting moon. It was down on the edge of the clouds and in a moment would be gone. He felt like a man hurrying down from a bleak mountain-top to a populous valley, and relief at feeling the distance shortening between himself and the first point of civilisation distorted the realities of the situation. He had no wish to remind himself that this civilisation consisted of no more than some 4000 men and a few women in small settlements on the shores of an icebound fjord, the snow lying deep around them, and two months to go to sunrise.

Now the flight seemed once more under control. The fuel check showed that the plan was working out to within a few pounds, and that they could count on getting to their advanced base with half an hour's endurance. Soon they could look out and hope to see the lights of Isfjord glowing through the cloud that swirls in from the warm sea to the west. That would be something solid to get hold of—a visual check of position—or so Peter reasoned ; although his navigators would have repudiated the idea that his identification of a ground object and his estimate of its bearing and distance could have any navigational significance at that height.

He peered out into the dark below, but had seen nothing when he was recalled to his responsibilities by the warning that they must steady for the next series of sextant shots. By now the Canberra was perfectly trimmed, although as it grew lighter and climbed there was less steerage-way and a tendency to wallow about on meeting small disturbances. In spite of this he managed to hold steady for the first two sights, but as the team started on the third the aircraft began to jar and bump like a car driven over the cobblestones. Tom was at the sextant and he swore as he tried to chase the bubble round its chamber ; he knew that the accuracy of the sight was jeopardised by the inability of the sextant controls to keep pace with the movement of that small circle of light. Peter also had to work hard as he tried to hold his heading and damp down the rougher oscillations. His only consolation was the memory of something he had been told by other crews who had passed this way ; they had always met this roughness over Spitsbergen, and looked on it as the island speaking to them through the air-currents disturbed by the rugged contours of the mountains.

They completed the series with relief, and as he relaxed to wait for the result Peter looked out and down. Close under the cockpit coaming, perhaps only five miles to one side, was an unmistakable glow on the cloud. As he watched, a slight thinning let him glimpse the blurred outline of individual lights, just like the street-lamps he had seen through the swirling fog as a child in London. There was the sudden change from an amorphous cloud of light to a sort of definiteness and back again.

Almost at once the fix came up to identify the settlement they had seen as Barentsberg, and to tell them that in just an hour's time they could hope to speak to a Norwegian radio station to ask how the weather had changed during the past six hours. The next stretch of ocean was as far across as from Iceland to Scotland and far more deserted, but by contrast with the distance they had already covered it felt like the run home across the English Channel. Twice more the team ran through the navigation routine and noted with satisfaction how the ground speed and fuel consumption were sticking to the plan. Although the moon had gone down, the aurora was stretched across the sky ahead like an aerial finishing-line, and by chance was in a position close to the first point at which they entered radio range of the coast of Norway.

At last Tom's voice, low and rather flat with fatigue, came through with the words Peter had been waiting for, restraining his impatience so as not to create the wrong atmosphere by seeming to ' flap '—

" Navigator to captain. Will you give them a call now?"

Peter turned his torch to illuminate the frequency-card fixed to the cockpit wall, noted the frequency of the station nearest to them and turned the radio selector knob click by click until he reached the point required. He waited a minute or two, pressed the button on the control-column, and transmitted in English to the station he hoped would hear—

" Helper control—this is Mike Golf Uniform Whisky Charlie—Do you read?"

He was not surprised to get no reply at first. Although they were theoretically within range he knew that freak effects often reduced the effectiveness of his transmissions or of the other station's replies. Just as a precaution he turned on the stand-by radio to let it warm up and repeated his call. Pressing his earpieces to his head he listened intently and was about to call again when he heard—

" Mike Golf Uniform Whisky Charlie—Helper Control —Do you read?"

Delighted, he answered and asked for the weather report, but on switching back to listen he heard the Norwegian operator repeating his call in the routine voice of one who has no idea that his message has been received. This was annoying, because it was evident that his own transmissions were not getting through, and without a weather report and good contact he could not venture to descend among the mountains of the advanced base. He looked at the fuel-gauge, which by now showed less in the tanks than he usually like to have at the end of a training flight at home. There would be enough to get to the main base if everything went to plan, but nothing in hand for searching without radio aids for the airfield.

Geoffrey had heard that contact did not seem to be successful, but he was not particularly put out, having great faith in his own navigational processes and some scorn for such single-seater aids as the airfield homer. He took Peter's decision to go for the main base in his stride, and set to with Tom to work out by dead-reckoning a point to begin the descent. By now the Canberra was like an almost empty fuel-drum with wings, and had in consequence drifted up to an altitude of over 50,000 feet. The descent from here had to be begun more than a hundred miles from their destination, so that it was not long before the time shown against a symbol on the chart came up and he was able to approve Tom's call to the pilot—

"Descend now."

They all knew that this was a critical moment. There would not be enough fuel to climb up again, and the descent made it impossible to get another accurate fix of their position with the sextant. Because of the heavy fuel consumption of the jet engines at low level they could not go many miles to correct errors in navigation that only became apparent after they broke cloud and could see the beam of the lightship or the lights of a town. The only safe approach was over the sea, and each one of them had a mental picture of the cold sea breaking over the half-submerged rocks on the approach to the runway. They separately, but fervently, prayed that radio contact would be established in time to make the last vital corrections to heading that bring one through the cloud on the shortest path to the airfield.

Peter looked down ahead, trying to see the lights of a town. A faint glow was tinging the tops of the clouds: he traced that to the moon. It was startling to realise that the speed of the Canberra was presenting him with a second moonrise on the same night; but all the good its light did was to show him, by the shape of the tops of the clouds, that snowstorms lay below and that no light could be expected to penetrate such dense masses of swirling white.

The situation looked bleak, but he had hopes of the stand-by radio. Once again he called, but this time there was not even the routine call to be heard, so he turned back to the main set to find out if any instructions were being broadcast. To his delight he found that his call on the other set had got through. For some reason he could only transmit on one set and receive on the other, but now that he knew how things were this was no worse than an inconvenience. He could deal with the situation if the people on the ground were on their toes ; and on this his confidence was boosted by the knowledge that his progress was now being followed by a Norwegian colonel with more D.F.C.s than most R.A.F. aces possess. The colonel would be watching every move from the control position on the ground, projecting his imagination into the boxful of luminous instruments that was rushing down towards the clouds, and getting himself into the minds of the men who were watching the dials. He would use this knowledge to advise the controllers on how to help in a case in which they had no such vivid personal picture to give life and validity to their reasoning.

Peter transmitted on the second set to say that he was receiving the ground-station and then returned quickly to the first box to get his reply. He sensed the relief in the voice of the controller who gave him the bearing, and was grateful for the fellow-feeling that prompted it in one whose secure surroundings might have cut him off too effectively from what was going on above.

Meanwhile Tom and Geoffrey, sceptical as ever of the efficiency of the homer, were comparing their dead-reckoning with the headings Peter was being given to steer. Not until he got the ' overhead ' from the homer and they found that it reconciled with the timing they had worked out would they give it full credit and relax somewhat. Even then they carefully scrutinised each instruction he was given, treating it with a healthy scepticism until it had passed the tests they applied to it. Their approving comments were a comfort to Peter, who by now had ceased to check on his fuel-gauges, because he knew that they were reading below the point at which he had any choice but to make a success of the first approach.

The critical moment for them all was as they completed their turn inwards to the 'safety lane' and plunged on down through cloud, the altimeter needle unwinding rapidly and giving a reading well below the height of the nearby mountains. Suddenly a glow of light came up ahead and almost at once turned into a clear double line of runway lights about five miles away. With relief Peter levelled out and lost speed, lowered his wheels and gratefully noted the thump and rumble as each leg came down in turn. He threw down the flap selector lever and felt the pressure of his shoulder-straps as the great barn-door area of the flaps caught the 150-knot wind. Almost at once, it seemed, the Canberra was floating down to the runway ; the engines were throttled fully back and the reflections of the runway lights, multiplied many times by the curved surfaces of the plastic canopy, were racing upwards across his view. The impression of speed was there for the first time since the take-off, but was gone almost at once as they grazed the runway, settled on and slowed down.

Back in the heated hangar the three climbed stiffly out and acknowledged our welcome. Their many layers of clothing were now keeping the warmth out more effectively than they had kept the cold at bay, so they rapidly stripped down to the comfort of string vests and long underwear before lighting their cigarettes. 'Debriefed,' warm and changed, they joined us in the wagon to drive to the town for a meal. As he looked back at the closing doors of the hangar Tom evidently felt that mists of unreality were already veiling his experiences.

The neon signs up the main street and the crowds in the foyer of the cinema completed his disillusionment. Then, as we turned towards the café, a break in the clouds caught his eye. Through it streamed the rays of his second moon since lunch-time ; beyond the search-lights of the aurora the pole star sat motionless and unregarded in the sky. He caught my eye and smiled with the confidence of the initiate.

"Come on," he said. "Let's have a beer."

[' Maga ' January 1957.

8

SKYDIVING
John Allen

It was quite by chance that I met Brodie Harrel, president of the Midnight Sun Skydivers. He was working in the Bureau of Land Management Forestry office on the outskirts of Fairbanks, Alaska, when I went in to sign up to fight the forest fires. In 1956 Brodie had played host for two nights to a party of British Army mountaineers led by Jimmy Mills. They had been climbing Mount McKinley. I had known Jimmy in Egypt in 1953 when we were both in the Parachute Brigade and, so, as the saying goes, ' we got talking,' Brodie and I. One thing led to another and, before I knew what I was saying, I had agreed to go jumping with him at the first opportunity. Two days later I was called out on the Tok-Kan fire and spent forty-six days in the bush. In the end I was in the wilds for practically the whole summer, and did not get a chance to meet Brodie again until the very beginning of September. Then I had a few days to kill in Fairbanks, and the idea of going jumping appealed to me once more. But this was to be parachuting with a difference. No Army-style line-ups, comfortable seats in large aeroplanes, static lines and well-marked dropping zones. This was to be skydiving, free-fall parachuting, something I had longed to do for many years.

Man has always wanted to fly, and the legend of Icarus was almost certainly based on an early failure to imitate the birds. Some great men such as da Vinci and Bacon, and others not so well known, like Fleyden and da Lanca, have drawn out on paper flying-machines, aerial boats and propeller-driven balloons. Lilienthal was the first to introduce the idea of curving the lifting or supporting surfaces, and he did not kill himself until he had made more than two thousand safe glides. When the Wright Brothers harnessed the engine to a flying-machine, and Santos-Dumont had flown two hundred and fifty yards in twenty-one seconds, the air age had arrived, and with it a widespread need for parachutes. Da Vinci's note-books contain parachute-drawings, and another pioneer inventor, Sebastien Lenormand, is said to have obtained his idea from the common jellyfish. In 1785 Blanchard dropped a dog from a balloon, and in 1793 he himself broke a leg in a parachute landing. Another Frenchman, Garnerin, gave exhibitions of jumping from balloons in France and England in 1802 from heights up to eight thousand feet. Towards the end of the First World War pilots were escaping from their planes by parachute, and its efficiency became a commonplace when parachute regiments were formed to conduct a specialised form of air-to-ground offensive in the Second World War. After 1945 clubs sprang up in France, Russia and the Balkan countries to practise parachuting.

The sport of skydiving, as it is now called, is young in America and even younger in England ; but it is growing fast. Skydiving is not a daredevil act to see how long a man can fall free before he pulls the ripcord. It is a sport with rules and regulations, with a beginning, a middle and an end. It has various manœuvres to be completed in the air, and these require much practice. One cannot say too strongly that skydiving is a safe sport, not a daredevil crowd-thriller.

In Alaska there are two flourishing clubs which combine the sport of skydiving with first-aid drops into inaccessible places. My parachuting experience before going to Alaska had been limited to eighteen jumps with the Parachute Regiment, all ' static line' jumps. For these the parachute is attached to a length of webbing, the static line, which is hooked to a wire in the aeroplane. All the parachutist has to do is to jump out: his parachute opens automatically, leaving the static line behind.

The day Brodie and I settled on to skydive was warm, and there was only a mild three- or four-knot breeze blowing up the slow-moving, muddy Chena River. Nothing to worry about here. We drove down the track by the railway-sidings to the small grass field and stopped by one of the hangars. " That's her." Brodie nodded towards a brightly-painted yellow Cessna 180 with red lines. We put our two backpacks on the grass verge and the two smaller spare 'chutes beside them. I did a couple of practice rolls on the hard earth and found that I had not forgotten everything I had learned. Brodie went off, and came back with the pilot to check over the plane. He beckoned me over and sat on the floor beside the pilot, with his legs hanging over the side. " It's all you have to do," he said with a grin. " Just sit here and topple right out." He jumped to the ground and I sat with my feet over the side and rocked myself off. " Of course, there'll be a bit of wind, but that's all there is to it," he said approvingly, as I rolled easily forward over the side of the plane. We walked back to our parachutes and put them on. Brodie helped me into the unfamiliar harness and hooked the spare 'chute onto the two 'D' rings on my chest. It was the first time I had worn a spare, for in the British Army the use of a reserve is a recent innovation.

The breeze, which was barely noticeable as we crossed the Chena, had faded completely, and the sun seemed to have the heat of mid-July in it as the dusty grass absorbed its glare. A mechanic sitting on an ice-chest full of Coca-Cola was sucking the remains of a drink from a bottle. He shook his head. "Crazy," he said. "You guys must be crazy." At this stage I was inclined to agree with him; but on these occasions the upper lip inevitably stiffens, and I managed a rather hearty, "Jolly good day for jumping." This produced a loud guffaw and a few choice remarks about the mad English, which did not help my waning confidence. Why was I doing it, anyway? The whole thing was senseless. At that point the engine of the Cessna shattered the still air and a funnel of dust rose up. Brodie came over with a helmet he had borrowed from the local high-school football team, and I put it on and fiddled with the strap. I could feel my hands shaking, and the damned strap would not go through the buckle. Brodie of course was ready before I had put the helmet to my head. He did up the buckle for me and I contrived a grin.

"Let's go," he said. My legs grew heavier and heavier as we approached the vibrating plane, my stomach did a loop all by itself, and all the time the plane was getting nearer and nearer. But before I knew what was happening I was being helped in and we were taxying down to the west end of the field. In the shade of the pines we turned and stopped, the plane pulsating, straining against the brakes. For a fleeting second I contemplated jumping out on to the dear earth, but I vaguely remembered that when I was in the Army this was just what I had wanted to do before *every* jump. I had always turned round to the men, stuck up my thumb and yelled something profane or asinine, like, "Here we go!" and there had always been a few acknowledging smiles. So I turned to Brodie and shouted, "This is it, I guess!" "You bet," he replied, and we were thrown back as the pilot released the brakes and the plane surged forward. Faster, faster, faster over the ground we bumped, and I knew now that there was no getting out. The pilot lifted the Cessna up and above the trees and swung her round in a wide climbing arc over Fairbanks.

I fingered my chinstrap nervously, pulled it a little tighter, and managed a sickly smile at Brodie who was glancing through the window. He smiled back and we made ourselves as comfortable as we could for the few remaining minutes. On the ground we had discussed how the descent should be made. This was the plan: the plane would fly the length of Cramer's field and over the middle of it. As we approached the first hedge I would slip my legs over the side and sit on the floor, holding onto the door-jambs. Brodie would be looking over my shoulder, and when he yelled 'Go' all I had to do was to let go and roll forward out of the door, wait half a second, then very firmly with my right hand pull the handle of the ripcord which was over on the left of my chest.

We had laughed and joked about it on the ground. As we circled Fairbanks at one thousand, then fifteen hundred feet, it was no longer a laughing matter. Brodie looked out of the side of plane and yelled. "There's the field." I nodded dumbly. When the pilot reached the required three thousand feet he set his course for the run-in. He nodded over his shoulder at Brodie as the field came under us. Brodie leaned over the side, and as the first boundary hedge passed directly beneath us he pulled me forward by the shoulder and gave me an encouraging nod. I slithered forward over the floor, now too frightened to think. I sat down on the floor, next to the pilot, with my legs facing the open door, and forced myself forward. It seemed to be blowing a gale, and as I pushed my legs out and over the side I was practically swept away. I clutched at the side of the door and looked down at the alien earth so far away. I remembered thinking that this was sheer madness. I saw Brodie over my right shoulder, leaning out, and suddenly he turned and yelled in my ear, "Okay—GO!"

I put my head down and rolled off the edge of the little plane with my eyes tight shut. The wind whipped me away. I remember thinking quickly that my eyes were closed and that I had better open them. When I did so I saw that my feet were together and pointing at the tail of the plane as it continued on over the field. My body turned and rolled in the air and my feet seemed to describe a slow circle round the disappearing tail of the Cessna. I looked down at the ripcord ring and grasped it firmly, and gave it the biggest tug I could muster.

The canopy fluttered out, billowed, breathed and mushroomed, and I looked up and grinned. "My first free fall," I said out loud. I put the ripcord on my wrist and looked up at the canopy, each panel filling out, alternately red and white. The field was large and I pulled on the lift-webs to guide myself as near as I could to the waiting car on the road. Remembering the instructors' old cry of 'feet and knees together', I locked my legs, and before I had quite realised it I was bumped hard, but safely, on the ground.

I took off my harness and patted the ground ; then rolled up the parachute and strode triumphantly off the field to receive the congratulations of the two fellows with the car. The Cessna came over the field again on the same track, but higher in the sky. We could see Brodie poised in the open door, his legs driven towards the tail by the wind. Then he rolled out and spread his arms and legs. This spread-eagle effect pulled him up into a stable position and he fell straight for ten seconds before his right hand flashed across his chest and the parachute blossomed out above him. It was the first free fall I had ever seen and I was fascinated. When Brodie joined us by the car he said it was nothing, and that one day we would go up to twelve thousand feet and do a forty-second or even a sixty-second delay jump, with turns and figure-eights, perhaps trying to pass a baton between us. "That's really skydiving," he said.

I was very happy that night in Tommy's Elbow Room on Second Avenue, where we went in celebration. Every first-timer stands a round of drinks and must himself have a Flaming Mamie, a liqueur-glass brimful of vodka, which is lighted. I had a large beard and did not want this to suffer the degradation of burning or even singeing, so I wiped my moustaches and carefully brushed the beard away from my mouth with a wet bar-towel as Tommy set the drink before me. I kept the towel by my left hand as he lit the vodka with a blow-torch. I am sure he must be the only bar-tender in the world to have a blow-torch on hand to 'flambeau' a customer's liqueur.

The vodka flickered and then caught, burning with a quiet, light-mauve flame. This was almost worse than skydiving ; but I grasped the glass firmly, took a deep breath, opened my mouth as wide as I could, and all but swallowed the glass too.

After our good start the weather turned nasty for a few days, but on the first bright morning I telephoned to Brodie and we arranged to jump that afternoon. We were to go out one after the other from three thousand five hundred feet, and I was to try the sky-diving technique. I had the same fears, the same empty feeling in the pit of my stomach, the same wish to jump out of the plane as it bumped its way slowly over the rough grass. Paper and straw blew uncontrollably about in the back as the pilot pulled the small Cessna over the trees at the end of the airstrip. There was a slight wind this time. I was going to jump out over the farm buildings that lay scattered along one side of the field ; this would give Brodie ample room for his descent on the same run.

We climbed higher and higher as we circled Fairbanks. The old boom town, which first tasted the lust for gold in 1902 and has never forgotten it, looked small, stretching unequally on either side of the dirty Chena. We levelled out at three-and-a-half thousand and the pilot started his run-in. I squatted on the floor of the plane and pushed my legs out. They were immediately seized by the wind and swept tailwards, but this time I was prepared for it and clung to the door jambs tightly. Brodie made his way to my right, and now our legs were tugged sideways in unison. I shall always remember thinking of us as two little boys, sitting on a bridge with our legs swinging madly. I did not dwell on that thought long, because now I could see the farm buildings only three or four hundred yards ahead and below. I eased myself forward, looked over my knees, and waited for the buildings to come directly underneath. As they did so I ducked my head and, keeping my eyes open this time, rolled forward, at once spreading my arms wide, arching my back, raising my head again and spread-eagling my legs. I seemed to turn a little on my right side, but then straightened up and stayed that way, falling flat, looking straight downwards at the farmyard.

I did not notice whether or not I was holding my breath. The wind buffeted my hands and arms slightly and I found I could not keep them quite still. They seemed to flap up and down jerkily, but only for a matter of inches. I cannot remember the wind in my face at all, and yet after ten seconds of the fall I must have been travelling at about a hundred and twenty miles an hour. This feeling of falling is strange ; to be sure, you are falling fast, but you are not plummeting down in a hopeless uncontrollable drop. You seem to be, in some way, in control of your descent. Yet I had a sense of freedom in diving through the sky such as I had never experienced before. I felt that I now knew why the birds sing so happily.

I watched the farmyard with interest and saw cows and a cart or two quite clearly before I pulled the ripcord and my red-and-white canopy mushroomed out. I tugged hard and long at the lift-webs to steer myself away from the buildings, and landed near the road again. Brodie came down a hundred yards from me, and together we walked to the road. We were in high spirits, exhilarated by that sense of accomplishment which comes with success. And this was only the start. I was just beginning to learn the thrill of skydiving.

Next day I left and started on my journey back east—
with my blood up to learn more of the technique of this
wide-open and freedom-giving sport. I was armed with
the address of the captain of the American Parachute
Team, Jacques Istel, the man behind the drive to popu-
larise skydiving in the United States. The main centre
of skydiving in the east of America is now at Orange,
Massachusetts, but then it was at Goodhill Farm, near
Woodbury in Connecticut. Mr Pond, the owner of the
farm, had a Cessna, a number of parachutes, and two
sons and one daughter-in-law who were and still are
skydivers in their own right. One son was a member of
the United States team which went to Russia for the
championships in 1958.

I went to Goodhill on the first Saturday as we had
arranged by letter and telephone. When I joined Istel he
was already surrounded by a dozen university students
from Harvard, Princeton and Yale. My second-hand
parachute, which I had been given and then used in
Fairbanks, was not up to the standard of Istel's new and
excellent blank-gore parachutes, and very kindly he lent
me one of his own. Although the descent I made that
day was only a 'jump and pull' from twenty-two
hundred feet, I immediately realised the superior qualities
of the blank-gores over my ex-Army T-10.

In Alaska the whole set-up for parachuting was non-
chalant and casual, a care-free (though not careless)
affair. In New England it was different. Istel, very
properly, controlled the skydiving organisation. It was
he who showed us the refinements of the blank-gore
parachute. It was he who 'passed' us novices into the
next stage of free-falling. In fact, it was Istel who *taught*
us how to enjoy and make the most of our skydiving. His

technique for jumping out was quite different from that we had used in Alaska, and it is this technique that is now the recognised, if not the official way of leaving any small aircraft. Two Cessnas were used for jumping. One was fitted with a wooden step which stuck out sideways from the underside of the fuselage. On the run-in at the required height, the jumper swung himself out on his step, facing forward. Holding on tightly to the angled wing-strut, he could watch the ground very closely for his mark, which he had carefully selected beforehand. When it came directly beneath him, he spread-eagled his legs backwards and up, and arched his back at the same time. The wind would tear his hands off the strut, and he would be in a stabilised skydiving position before actually starting the descent. At least that is what should happen in theory. But in many of my descents I found that I had a tendency to roll over on to my right side and cartwheel slowly through the air; and this was only corrected after someone who was watching me carefully from the plane saw that when I jumped my arms were never truly level and that my right hand always dropped slightly.

The second Cessna was not fitted with a board outside, so the jumper placed his right boot on the landing-wheel (of course with the brake on), and his left boot on the foot-rest. The wheel was only slightly lower than the foot-rest, but the uneven placing of the feet did not affect the jumper or his position once he had left the aeroplane.

It was while jumping at Goodhill that I really began to learn about skydiving and its intricacies. A number of us had been doing five- to ten-second 'delays' and were beginning to be very confident, getting that know-all air, and eager to go on to the longer delays where stop-watches and altimeters have to be used. For it is only in a twenty-, thirty- or sixty-second delay that the true art of skydiving can be practised, when the jumper has time to complete his figure-eight, or whatever exercise he is carrying out, before pulling his ripcord.

One fine Sunday afternoon Istel and the second-string in the American team, Lew Sanborn, gave a demonstration jump from twelve thousand feet, and this, more than anything, whetted my appetite for more. A comparatively small number of people in the world have been that height in a light aeroplane, and very few with the intention of jumping out. Istel and Sanborn had discussed their timed criss-cross pattern through the sky. Each had a canister attached to one foot, which produced a trail of coloured smoke. Those of us on the ground watched enviously as the yellow-and-black Cessna took off into a cloudless sky with the two jumpers on board, both clad in white overalls and helmets, goggles and leather gloves. To their spare 'chutes, clipped to their chests, were attached the all-important stop-watches and altimeters. The small plane climbed steadily in circles for almost half an hour. For us, sitting on the grass in front of the hangar, the sun radiated summer heat on this breezeless autumn day, but we all knew that for the two jumpers and the pilot in the aeroplane it must have been cold and very windy, for the door had been removed before take-off. As the plane laboured higher and higher we on the ground knew what was going on in the small cabin. Neither of the parachutists would be saying a word, for the wind whips away all meaningful sound ; and both would be rubbing their hands and feeling thankful for the warmth of their gloves. At ten thousand feet the countryside around Goodhill would lose its

individual character and their world would be a pano-
ramic view that took in the neighbouring states of New
York and Massachusetts. One thing that would remain
clearly under their gaze was the small white cross, the
now tiny white cross, on the dropping-zone, looking from
twelve thousand feet like a pin-head. The pilot levelled
out, and I guessed that he would be shouting over his
shoulder that he was starting a long run-in. This would
give the two experts plenty of time to decide on their
exit, for the wind changes considerably in twelve thousand
feet. In my mind I was up there with them in the plane.
They nodded to each other, and Sanborn muttered an
unheard remark into his chin-strap. He clambered out
on the step, holding on tightly to the strut, and looked
down and ahead of him. He glanced at Istel, who had
slithered forward to the open door, and shrugged his
shoulders as if to say, 'It's so damned far up anyway,
what's a couple of seconds' difference going to make?'
He looked down again, and then thrust his head towards
the cabin where Istel was crouching ready to follow him
into the sky, "Five," he yelled, signifying that he was
going to jump in five seconds' time. Istel nodded and,
counting off the seconds, readied himself for his spring.
He saw Sanborn poised on the step, and then suddenly,
after the five seconds, he was no longer there but diving
through the sky. Istel launched himself after Sanborn,
and he could see Sanborn stabilised now and waiting so
that they could start their manœuvring together, one
above the other. Istel moved his arms slowly and
cautiously forward, for no movement can be hurried in
skydiving. And now, together, they began a series of
sweeps out and back again, criss-crossing as they plummeted through the sky. They looked with concentration

at the second-hands on their watches, timing each curve in the symmetrical pattern. The blue and red smoke twisted and spiralled in continuous streams behind them, marking the paths of their fall through the air. So accurate was the smoke-pattern woven by these diving men that it was as if some puppet-master was controlling them on unseen strings. They turned outwards once more, and then two canopies trailed simultaneously skywards, mushroomed, and blossomed to their perfect shape. Istel and Sanborn were two thousand feet up. There was a quiet, dazzled "Ah!" from us, like the first, soft, hopeful "Olé!" from the crowd watching a bull-fight. Then we clapped furiously as the two men, expertly working the rigging-lines, landed, one fourteen yards and the other twenty-two yards from the white cross. It was an exceptional performance from that great height, even for such experienced skydivers.

I could not help thinking afterwards of the thrill this fine spectacle would have given the old pioneer, Garnerin, had he been able to watch. In the early part of the nineteenth century he had no perfectly-balanced nylon canopies, but gave his demonstrations with a crude twenty-three-foot canvas canopy shaped like an umbrella and finished off at the top with a ten-inch wooden disc with a hole in it. Today, sport-parachutes have twenty-eight panels or gores, each a foot wide at the base. Each gore is made of three panels, running diagonally, so that a tear can only affect one third of one gore and the performance of the parachute is almost unchanged. In a blank-gore parachute, one panel is left out. The gap can be closed by pulling gently down on a side rigging-line, and this makes the parachute spin smoothly to left or right, as desired.

Some days afterwards we had a 'jump-and-pull' competition, and from a little over two thousand feet I managed to land within seventy yards of the cross. Not very good. Later I did three more jumps, each with ten-second delays. Then the first signs of winter came, in the form of high winds, and skydiving virtually ceased at Goodhill for the year. The next year found me back in Alaska, and, hopeful of more jumping, I contacted Brodie Harrell. But once more we were busy fighting fire, and I never did any jumping there again. But I still have hopes ; for it is what the earliest pioneers were after—and what man is learning to do—to turn and spiral, dip and plunge, truly to dive through the air with almost the freedom that belongs to the birds.

['Maga' October 1960.

9

THE BREATH OF LIFE

Group Captain A. G. Dudgeon, C.B.E., D.F.C., R.A.F.

Since the days when I left Cranwell and went to India as a Pilot Officer, the art of flying has changed immeasurably. You could then, if you wanted, jump into an aircraft and, with very little paraphernalia, fly ' by the seat of your pants '. The throttle, stick and rudder bar were the essentials ; the remaining things were largely aids. In a modern aircraft, much that you previously took entirely for granted has now become of vital concern. Take, for example, breathing.

The muscles of your body work because little electrical impulses are sent to them by the brain. As they move, they use up energy. Your eyes see because light causes impulses to be sent along the optic nerves: more energy required. The brain itself, master computer, organiser and director, also uses energy. There is one common denominator to all these functions of the human frame—oxygen.

At normal temperatures and pressures, the body takes air into the lungs at regular and frequent intervals. Each lungful contains a certain amount of oxygen. The blood, carried in a myriad tiny vessels near the internal surfaces of the lungs, gives up waste gases. Oxygen is forced into their place by the pressure. Thus, with the circulation of the blood, the necessary oxygen is carried all over the body.

As altitude is increased the air gets thinner ; there is less of it in each lungful inspired. This deficiency, by itself, could be made good by breathing faster. However, and this is the special point, the pressure is also reduced, and a time comes when there is insufficient pressure to force a full load of oxygen into the blood, no matter how quickly you breathe. There is also another complication. As the pressure goes down, the other gases in the air (nitrogen, for one) tend to take preference. They elbow oxygen out of the way, as it were, and stop the blood from getting a fair share. When the blood is not getting its full supply of oxygen, you suffer from what the doctors call ' anoxia '.

One way of preventing the onset of anoxia at height is to enrich the air with some extra oxygen fed in through a mask. There is a limit to this, however ; for above forty-two thousand feet there is not enough pressure for the blood to be revitalised, even when breathing one hundred per cent oxygen. Another method of helping a pilot is to seal him in the cockpit and pump up the pressure around him. In practice both methods are used ; for aircraft go too high to rely on oxygen-breathing alone, and the trick cannot be done solely by pumping up pressure in the cockpit without making it unreasonably strong and heavy.

Anoxic individuals vary greatly in their symptoms, and it is unwise to generalise about them too much. But by any standards anoxia is a most insidious complaint. It is often rather like drunkenness. The brain, that most delicate organ, is first affected. You feel cheerful. You feel clever when you are really becoming stupid. Next, the eyes tend to go peculiar. After that, the body muscles. The speed with which it affects you depends on how little oxygen is getting to the blood, and how long a time is available to become adjusted. At, say, fifteen thousand feet, breathing pure air, the effects can take an hour or so to be noticeable, and even then they are probably not very dangerous. At forty thousand feet unconsciousness in about thirty seconds and perhaps death in a few minutes. About four out of five people cannot detect anoxia in themselves. I am a lucky fifth. Having done photographic survey work in the nineteen-thirties, flying high without oxygen equipment, I can identify anoxia almost at once by the tingling in my fingertips. I learned this simply by trial and error ; the errors were there to see on the photographs afterwards. If flown too high, the runs were insufficiently accurate for maps to be made from the pictures. This meant another sortie, a bit lower, without my fingertips tingling so much.

Not long ago I was sitting in my office, ploughing through a N.A.A.F.I. report, when the telephone rang. It was 'Chick' Sparrow, one of the Squadron Commanders. " I've got a spare aircraft, sir," he said, " and I'm putting up some practice battle-formations. I thought perhaps you would like a trip. Take-off as soon as possible."

" Right," I answered, dropping the report like a stale cake. " Today I'll fly number two of a pair. One of your junior chaps can lead. By the way," I added, glancing across at the peg where my flying-kit hung, " can you lend me an oxygen mask? Mine has gone in for servicing."

"Sure," he answered, "borrow mine. I've got a job to do and won't be using it."

Grabbing my gear, I drove down to the Squadron crew-room. All the pilots were already kitted up and Chick was about to brief. "I will dress while you carry on," I said, and with a brief acknowledgment he began to outline the technicalities of our respective sorties. In methodical haste I began to change. First, the anti-G suit. Slipping off my trousers, I zipped, buckled and laced up this very expensive form of inflatable corset. It connects by a tube to the aircraft's pneumatic system and, when you make violent manœuvres, it squeezes your body like a man gripping a toothpaste tube in his fist, thereby preventing centrifugal force from draining blood away from your brain. Thus you can retain consciousness and vision in combat. An important factor. Next, overalls ; then Mae West and boots. Having clipped the borrowed oxygen mask to the inner cloth helmet, and clutching my 'bone dome' and gloves, I was ready to go.

While this was happening, I had learned that my leader was Oaky, a flying-officer whom I knew well, a cheerful individual, the Squadron wag and an able pilot. Our callsigns, Yellow One and Yellow Two. The weather was not too good at the lower levels—a dreary day with about a thousand-foot cloud base and then almost solid to twenty thousand feet or so. Above that, clear blue and sunshine all the way, which was where we were going. Oaky needed no practice at leading. Also, he was no slouch ; I was obviously going to be made to work for my living.

In the crew-room we signed the authorisation book.

From there we went to the flight office and signed the maintenance record. And so out to the aircraft. Oaky discussed a few detailed points with me on the way and, having walked slowly round my Hunter for a final check-over, I climbed up the access ladder and entered the cockpit.

Allow, say, five minutes for strapping in and start-up. Avoid a mad rush, but no time to be wasted. First, each leg and shoulder parachute-strap to be clipped into the quick-release box. An airman stands on the access ladder to help you. Then the seat-harness, four more straps to hold you firmly in place, even when the aircraft is inverted. Then the oxygen-tube, and the emergency oxygen-tube. I noticed that Chick's connector was rather stiffer to join up than my own, but it appeared to click home all right and a quick tug seemed to indicate that it was quite secure. The airman plugged the radio connections into place behind my left shoulder. Then the bone dome came down over the inner cloth helmet and we were ready, isolated effectively from the outside world except by signs and radio. The airman gave me the thumbs up with an enquiring look and got a brief nod in reply. He took the safety-pin out of the ejector-seat cartridge and held it in front of my face. Another nod to show I knew the seat was 'live' and he stowed the pin in its socket behind my left elbow. Finally, with a friendly grin to wish me *bon-voyage,* he climbed down the ladder, removed it and stood clear.

Busying myself in the cockpit, I did all the pre-start checks and adjustments, leaving only the fuel cocks, master electric switch and starter-button still to be operated. I looked across at Oaky in the next aircraft. He had beaten me through the routine, and was already waiting. *Touché!* Seeing my affirmative thumbs up, he raised one finger to roughly the level of his eyebrow and gave a little twirl. Start up. Fuel on, electrics on, press starter-button. The cordite starter-cartridge roared and the rev. counter began to wind up. In a moment or so the jet-pipe temperature-gauge was reading, showing that the motor had 'torched' correctly and the fire was properly alight inside. By the time the last few checks were done and the remaining warning lights had gone out, the familiar hiss in my earphones showed that the radio valves had warmed up. Oaky's voice, disembodied, somewhat distorted, but plainly recognisable, said: "Yellow Two, check in." "Yellow One, fives," I answered, and "Yellow section, Baker," came back. Exchange of information has been reduced to the absolute minimum in words and time. Strength and quality are reported on a scale from one to five. One word, 'fives,' told Oaky that his transmitter and my receiver were working well. The fact that he passed me back the word 'Baker' not only confirmed the effectiveness of the two-way system from my end, but also warned me that we were to change frequency to the channel identified by the letter 'B' on the control box. I changed frequency, and checked in again to prove that I had done so.

I heard Oaky call control for taxi-clearance and then followed him out as he rolled towards the end of the runway. A minute or so later we were tearing down the vast expanse of concrete, only a few feet between our machines. I felt the nose-wheel lift, then the whole aircraft, and at last our wheels were up and locked away. Swinging round to the south we picked up speed and began the long climb, entering cloud as we did so.

Streaking along and upwards at nearly four hundred

miles an hour in light fog, you must stay close. If you lose sight of your leader in a mist, there is nothing to do but to pull well clear and climb through it alone, and then try to make contact again in the clear air above. Which wastes time and is therefore most unpopular with the leader. At last, at about twenty thousand feet, gleaming wetly, we popped out into the sunshine. I relaxed and opened out formation to check round the cockpit. In particular, the oxygen. Tube and emergency tube plugged in; contents gauge, satisfactory; the luminous 'blinker' opening and closing as each breath was drawn in; aircraft altitude twenty-two thousand feet, and the cockpit 'altitude' much lower, showing that the air around me was being compressed properly.

By this time we were well south of base and approaching an area usually containing 'trade' in the form of a few American fighters. These could normally be expected to accept a challenge and, once combat had been joined, it was a question of devil take the hindmost.

Sure enough, as we reached forty-five thousand feet, pressurised in the cockpits to twenty-six thousand feet, we could see two condensation trails cutting across the deep blue, and obviously caused by two other specks on a course to intercept. I checked the camera gun. As they closed, Oaky swung us into a turn towards them. Now our combined closing speed was up to about a thousand miles an hour. Soon we were all twisting and turning like minnows among the reeds, glinting and gleaming in the brilliant sunlight, colours looking twice as bright against the royal blue of the high-altitude sky. Four men, each doing all he knew to position his machine so that it could bring back the tell-tale camera-gun photograph. And avoiding, too, giving that opportunity to an opponent. Oaky and I swung our aircraft round in the tightest circles we could, this way and that as he called the turns. Great forces were heaving at my body and the ' G ' suit was doing its work nobly, clamping my lower half as in a vice and stopping the blood from pooling in my legs. They were good, these two Americans in their Super Sabres, and they really made us work. In general we were outmanoeuvring them, but they had the edge on us in climb and speed.

As we came out of a very steep turn, I had dropped back a bit and was behind Oaky. The two Americans were one on either side of me, a hundred yards out and slightly ahead. I remember chuckling, for I thought I had them cold. If either turned in to attack Oaky, I would promptly fall in behind him for a sitting shot. If one turned away, I was perfectly placed to turn with him also. I sat there for a few moments, glancing from one to the other, revelling in the situation, waiting to see which would move first and become the sitting duck. Suddenly I realised that, as I looked at one of them, I could not see Oaky out of the corner of my eye as I should. When I looked towards Oaky, I lost sight of the Americans. The truth swept over me like a cold shower. My vision had become abnormal. Something must have gone wrong with my oxygen supply. Instantly the mock combat was dismissed. I glanced down, and saw that the end of my oxygen tube had pulled out and was hanging loose. I was breathing pure air. My fingertips were tingling like mad.

Having been concentrating on the battle, I had obviously failed to notice this for some time because, in hindsight, my reactions were not good. I must already have been fairly far gone. By my right side was a yellow knob, the emergency oxygen toggle. One pull, and all would have been well. But all I could think about was to get the main tube back in its socket. I knew, quite clearly at the back of my mind, that if I did not get oxygen again, quickly, I was going to die. I should become unconscious and the aircraft would fall out of control into nineteen thousand feet of cloud. If, by some freak, consciousness returned at the lower levels, the chance of regaining control, in cloud, on instruments, would be negligible. I *had* to get that tube back in place.

I left the aircraft to its own devices and, with one shaking hand which would not do my bidding as it should, I clasped the socket. With the other hand I fumbled for and eventually got the oxygen tube. I could not see properly. My sight was closing in fast and it was like looking through a keyhole. Somewhere in the distance I heard Oaky call me on the radio, but I could not spare a hand for the transmit-button on the throttle. At last I managed to get the two ends pointed together, and discovered that a spring-loaded dust cap on the socket was in the way. It would not go in. I cursed aloud at it, a stream of swear words. Using all my strength against the feeble spring I lifted it, and felt the tube enter the opening. Then came the effort to try and get it pushed home to make a gas-tight joint through which I could again draw the life-giving oxygen. Nothing I could do would make it go. By now there seemed to be a gauze veil in front of my eyes and I kept straining to open them wider. Although it felt as if something was fouling the joint, I could not see if this was really true. I knew full well that I had but a few seconds left.

On the oxygen-control panel, on the right-hand side of the cockpit, is a switch that will give an increased flow.

It supplies oxygen under pressure, instead of only when demanded by breathing. Holding the two ends of the oxygen connection together with my left hand, I tried to find this switch. I peered, seeking it ; but everything was now dark and grey, or black. Nothing whatever would focus. I felt my right hand pounding round the starboard console. I can remember touching and operating the fuel booster-pumps and then shaking my head to try and clear my addled brain. Somewhere, somehow, a voice was saying "Keep going," when my entire being just wanted to give up the unequal struggle. It did not seem fair that I should be subjected to this ghastly battle with circumstances.

At last, I got it. I felt the square-ended switch, and, blessed relief, felt it click across under my fingers. Now the oxygen should be coming in, and if it did not, I had shot my bolt. I sat back, exhausted, concentrating solely upon keeping the two ends of the connector held together.

I do not know how long it took. First, the daylight came back as the lights go up in a cinema. I was in darkness and then, moments later, it was broad daylight. I was still above cloud, but fifteen thousand feet of height had vanished somewhere. With perfect ease I clicked the connections firmly together and felt the blessed oxygen rippling round the edges of my mask. I had won. Then I got an uncontrollable fit of ague, and dreadful shivers up and down my spine which lasted for probably five to ten seconds. To take my mind off the situation, I reached for the transmit-button and called Oaky. I told him I had had oxygen failure but was all right now, though still a bit groggy. Feeling rather shamefaced, I asked him to shepherd me home.

To hear Oaky's calm reply, saying he had wondered

what was up and telling me where to look in the sky for him was a wonderful restorer. Apart from a continuing prickling in the small of my back as the realisiation of just how close it had been sank in, I felt almost human. I set about the business of overhauling the little speck in the distance that was Oaky.

Fear is an interesting emotion. During the critical period I had no sense of fear whatever. It would be nice to suggest that romantic notions such as thoughts of my ever-loving wife and family spurred me on. Not a bit of it. It had been coldly clear in my mind that it was even money, or worse, that death would come to me in two or three minutes. It was equally clear that it could only be avoided by achieving the immediate task in the little time I had. The difficulties provoked concern, frustration and anger ; not fear. Afterwards, when the fight had been won and life seemed to stretch ahead again to infinity, there was a terrific reaction. That, I suppose, might be called fear.

It was a chastened character who strolled across the tarmac to sign off in the various books. Twenty-four years' flying, and then to get caught like that! Perhaps a little too much haste and not enough attention to detail. The plain horse-sense of having one's own flying-kit, knowing it, and not borrowing any unknown or unfamiliar item. So, also, the oft-repeated dictum of practising and being so familiar with the emergency drills that the *right* one is an instinctive reaction when the time comes. These were warnings I had often plugged to my juniors, and now it was my own ears which had been deaf. Being a pilot is superbly exhilarating, but it can also be a harsh trade and, sometimes, unforgiving.

"Oaky," I said, "I am going to the Mess because I think now I would enjoy a glass of beer. How about you?"

"Sir," he answered, "I *always* enjoy a glass of beer."

['Maga' August 1959.

10

THE CUMULO-NIMBUS CLOUD

James Thomson

" Here's your forecast, gentlemen," said the Met. man. He pinned the chart on the wall of the briefing room. The crew looked at the chart and their interest sharpened as they saw the close-set isobars and the curving red and blue lines of the fronts.

" I've drawn in your route," the Met. man continued. " St Eval, Start Point, Cherbourg, Marseilles, bottom of Sardinia and along to Malta." His finger traced the line across the chart.

" Fairly good most of the way, just a spot of bother over the French Massif as usual. This north-westerly airstream is very unstable and with lifting over the high ground will give thunderstorms."

" How wide is the thunderstorm activity likely to be?" asked the pilot.

" About fifty miles, I'd say. They should be fairly scattered, but you may run into a large patch." He beamed at the airmen jovially and droned on about winds, icing index, freezing level and the present and forecast weather along the route.

Later, while they were flight-planning, the navigator

asked: " Do you want me to plan a diversion through the Carcassone gap, Skipper, in case the cu-nims are too bad?"

" No, I don't think so," said the pilot. " If we meet any that seem too bad we can dodge between them."

In the pilot's mind ideas about the flight took shape. Height nine thousand five hundred feet: no need to change that, it was the safety height above all high ground along the route, the best height for engine performance, and comfortably below the freezing-level. If thunderstorms appeared, the dreaded cumulo-nimbus clouds, then it was better to be above the lower clouds and in the clear night sky where the towering cu-nims would show up and so be avoided. Moving round the flight-planning room he checked the latest information on danger areas and air traffic procedures. The navigator worked out the headings, ground speeds and times.

After take-off, the pilot climbed the aircraft on course for Start Point and levelled off at nine thousand five hundred feet. The night sky was clear and lit by thousands of stars spread out above. Below, England lay asleep with only the street lamps awake and holding hands in lonely crescents and avenues. One or two cumulus clouds floated along like errant cauliflowers. Beyond Start Point the Channel heaved darkly, rocking the steamers whose lights winked back brazenly at the stars. Cherbourg was ablaze with neon glow and France opened out ahead, the bright towns signposting the way.

The pilot sat easily at his controls, the auto-pilot controller under his right hand, the throttle and r.p.m. levers under his left. He looked ahead and to port and starboard, searching the sky for lights and clouds ; lights which could mean another aircraft on a collision course ;

clouds which could mean storms. Below the coaming, included every few seconds in the ceaseless travel of the pilot's eyes, the fluorescent faces of the instruments gave him the reaction of the machine he guided. The flight instruments showed him the position and movement of the machine in space, the height, course and airspeed. The engine instruments showed him that the four motors were providing the power to keep him and his forty passengers in the air.

Yet, while his eyes and hands and his trained reactions controlled and guided the aircraft, he was unconscious of it in a strange way. He sat in his seat and was completely relaxed, motionless except for his right hand which, now and then, made an alteration to the aircraft's attitude by moving the small lever of the auto-pilot. He did not think about the alteration in terms of ' slight dive, ease back ' or ' one degree off heading, turn right one degree '. His eyes took in the data from the instruments, his brain accepted the problem and answered it by moving his fingers in the necessary way. But he did not consciously think about the problem. The essential part of the pilot, his mind, his ego, was apart from the process of maintaining straight and level flight. It was like an immaterial system of ideas, thoughts, questions and answers floating along, disembodied, in the night sky. The stars were its companions, the clouds its neighbours and the limitless space its dominion. A pure system of ideas speculating on its existence and its environment, on the way ahead, the storms and the peacefulness of the sky ; oblivious of the thirty tons of steel, light alloy, blood and bone surrounding it, and somehow, not really concerned with the material presence of itself, yet immersed in the problem of transporting itself and the material to the destination.

The idea system communed within itself in a manner born of many nights in the wide darkness and about the same problems. The fascination was that each time the conditions were slightly different. A continuous interrogation went on in the pilot's head.

'There are some clouds ahead which could be the beginning of a cold front.'

'True, but they may be local stuff.'

'Thunderstorms are only local stuff.'

'We'll see the anvils first and the lightning. The cloud ahead is not very high, not much above our level and we're going to miss them anyway.'

'There are always thunderstorms over the French Massif at this time of year.'

'We'll miss them.'

'Don't kid yourself, you've been lucky with cu-nims so far, but you're about due to hit one.'

'Superstition.'

'The clouds are closer now and towering above our level. See that anvil over there, slightly port? That's a big one, brother, lucky it's on the port bow.'

'I've told you, we'll miss them.'

'That line of cloud looks awful solid to me. You can't go over, you can't go under, you gotta go through.'

'There is no physical impossibility about flying through a cumulo-nimbus cloud. This aircraft is strong enough, we have a sufficient reserve of power. It might be unpleasant for a few minutes but that is all.'

'Listen to the dauntless aviator stuff. Who do you think you're kidding? These clouds are rough babies: vertical gusts of thousands of feet a minute, that's not funny. And what about icing? Remember old Davies, the Met. man at Feltwell, he drilled it into his students, icing may occur anywhere in a cumulo-nimbus cloud, severe icing, above or below the freezing level. And five minutes of severe icing and you'll be fluttering down like a plucked chicken.'

'Let us look at this icing bogey. It is unlikely that the ice will build up at more than one inch in five minutes. Our de-icing system is inefficient but it will prevent a certain amount of icing. We can take, perhaps, two or three inches; that gives us ten to fifteen minutes. Our ground speed is one hundred and eighty knots so we travel thirty to forty-five miles. It is most unlikely that any thunderstorm is more than thirty miles in extent. We're fireproof.'

'Well—look ahead. I hope you're right.'

The pilot looked ahead at the cloud-mass building up before him and saw dense, black and grey mountains looking solid and menacing in the misty starlight. The tops were high above any altitude he could hope to reach, and in the middle levels the outlying towers and castles of cloud changed shape, writhing and twisting before his eyes. He sensed the vast, imponderable forces at work within the cloud—forces large enough to hold in suspension thousands of tons of water in tiny droplets, enough to flood a town. Nature's chamber-pots poised to plash on the innocent aviator. And Nature was demonstrating her atom bombs too: away on either hand lightning flickered along a line of exploding and pulsating cloud pillars which swept up to the heavens.

Nodding to himself the pilot examined his situation. Ahead, probably at about twenty miles, a line of cumulo-nimbus clouds was grunting away over the high massif of France. The highest ground within twenty miles of the aircraft's track was six thousand feet. At nine thousand five hundred feet he had ample clearance, but he could not descend to pass below the storm. Alternatively, he could not climb above the clouds for their tops were above his ceiling. He must try to pass between the storm centres.

The lightning was crackling about the tips of the leaden clouds, incredibly beautiful tracery outlined in yellow fire as the electricity shot to and fro across the vapour trails outlying the main cloud-body. Almost on course there was a valley in the cloud wall, a lesser bank between two summits whose fiery majesty stood out against the darker immensity of space. The pilot considered that the aircraft would still enter cloud but it would not be the full violence of the storm.

His course resolved, the pilot made a few dispositions within the aircraft.

" Captain to crew. We are going to pass between two cumulo-nimbus clouds. There may be some turbulence which may last for about ten minutes. See that all passengers are strapped in and all loose equipment stowed. Turn up the cockpit lighting and, Engineer, prime the de-icers."

" De-icers on, Captain," replied the engineer.

" Co-pilot, give me twenty-four hundred revs. We'll increase to turbulence speed." The pilot was conscious that his voice was flat and held in. " And tell the signaller to earth his trailing aerial."

The orders given, the pilot felt that he had disposed the crew to meet any threat. He switched off the auto-pilot, retrimming the aircraft to give himself a comfortable feel of the controls. He pulled at his straps until he felt a good, solid tension, and settled his back firmly against the seat.

The first cloud-patches were moving towards the aircraft, slowly then with increasing speed until they suddenly erupted against the windscreen and the pilot needed all his will-power to keep from ducking down into the safety of his cockpit. He took one last look then concentrated on the instruments. There was a slight bump as the aircraft entered cloud, and the pilot's hands tightened on the controls. There was no further jolt, and he knew that the dangerous areas of the cloud were not yet near. He looked out for an instant at the cold, grey mass of the vapour pressing against the windscreen ; it was like a shapeless monster hungry to get in. To port and starboard the navigation lights blurred out in reflected ghostly spheres of red and green light. Tiny blue sparks flickered across the windscreen, first in the corners, then spreading over the oblong panel like an eerie ballet of gremlins. The propeller tips glowed softly with green flame and suddenly burst into a million leaping sparks as the St Elmo's fire grew up into long, waving lances and pennons. The pilot, entranced by this beauty, wondered how many sailors had seen and loved the green fire dancing over the masts and rigging. He felt exhilarated as he counted himself among the old company of mariners ; a good company, he thought, and stout in the heart.

The St Elmo's fire flickered silently and grew dim, and ceased. Darkness closed in and the pilot felt close to the heart of the storm. Weird lights flamed and died away, lightning in neighbouring storms. The darkness increased and soon there was no hint of light beyond the cockpit's brave shine, only an inky blackness more fearsome than the solitary night. The aircraft, as though alive, was trembling in the disturbed air. The pilot felt under his hands the control runs taking up the slack as the surfaces moved in sympathy with the eddies cast out by the tortured clouds.

Suddenly, a shock, the aircraft plunged and leapt like a frightened horse. A wing dropped and the pilot heaved the machine back on to an even keel. The artificial horizon showed that the aircraft was straight and level, but the altimeter was winding up like a crazy clock and the rate of climb showed two thousand feet a minute. Like a lift, the thought came into the pilot's head, going up like a lift. Old lessons came back to him ; in turbulence disregard the loss or gain of height, maintain the attitude, keep your aircraft level. ' Going up ; ladies' underwear ' ; the pilot repressed an insane giggle. Then he gasped as the seat fell away beneath him and the aircraft dropped like a stone, the control column kicking and twisting in his hands. The descent eased off into a turbulent buffeting and he struggled to maintain attitude.

A slow, piercing whistle built up and the pilot glanced quickly at the windscreen. Tell-tale ice crystals were forming on the glass.

" Check the de-icers, Engineer." He tried to sound unconcerned.

" De-icers on emergency, Captain." The engineer's voice was quiet and confident.

The pilot's arms were beginning to ache with the effort of holding the controls against the various tendencies of the aircraft to dive and yaw and climb as the currents of air tore at the fuselage and wings. The air-speed was slowly falling ; the de-icers were losing the battle against ice formation. He called for more power and checked the r.p.m. and boost gauges. The trembling needles told their tale of engine icing. The moments were endless and time seemed to have stopped in the maelstrom of the sky. Wave after wave of solid air hit the aircraft until it seemed to dance like a pine-cone in a mountain stream. The noise outside increased to a howl, blotting out the engine note as the airstream fluted between the ice crystals on aerials and canopy. Another sweep of air, forced into tremendous instability by the interaction of moisture, heat and the mountains below, rammed the aircraft upwards. The pilot fought to keep the nose down as some freak of the gust threatened to stand the machine on its tail. Just as suddenly the gust stopped and the aircraft plunged into a down current. Only his lap-strings biting into his thighs kept the pilot with the controls. Down, down, the thought echoed across the mind ; shall we splash, I wonder, shall we splash.

With a shuddering heave the aircraft spewed out of a cloud wall into the clear night sky. One or two parting jolts shook the control column as the pilot eased the machine back to nine thousand five hundred feet. He could not see through his windscreen for the ice, but surprisingly it was only a thin film. Switching on the screen de-icer he waited for the ice to clear. Rapidly the blown wash of alcohol swept the glass. The sky ahead was empty ; there was no cloud in sight. Below, the coastline unfolded like a vast, illuminated map. He could see Marseilles and the familiar flashing light of Sète. The pilot handed over control to the co-pilot and climbed stiffly from his seat. A cup of coffee was handed to him.

" How are we doing, Nav. ?" he asked.

" O.K. Skipper ; about five minutes ahead of E.T.A. That was a rough one. Did we go through the centre?"

" No, I don't think so," he replied. " Just round the edges."

[' Maga ' July 1964

11

'LEADS THE FIELD'

Wing-Commander K. P. Smales, D.S.O., D.F.C., R.A.F.

"England expects much of her servants, and quite rightly too," said the Ambassador. I suspect that he was speaking from personal experience as much as anything else, but at that moment he was watching four Canberra jet bombers climbing rapidly into the distance over the sea towards the Mexican coast. He may have been thinking of the pilot of the leading Canberra; for the Air Marshal was certainly an outstanding servant of England. Now, comfortably tucked into the cockpit at the controls of the Canberra, the Air Marshal's mind must have been fixed on the immediate problem in hand, that of keeping the aeroplane in the climb at the correct mach number. If at that moment he had any other thoughts at all, they were very likely of the Ambassador who had entertained him so well and whose sentiments he would have understood. Sentiments which would have been understood by the whole force of the seventeen officers and thirty airmen, twelve of them now airborne in the Canberras bound for British Honduras and Mexico City, and the remainder of us on the airfield at Maiquetia in the damp and salty heat of the Venezuelan coast. We were taking leave of our friends who had driven down that frightening, twisting road from the cool of Caracas to bid us farewell.

The captain of the Hastings transport aircraft had already started his number one engine. The Canberra servicing crews were aboard, and with a mingling of " Goodbyes " and " *Adios pues, hasta la vista,*" the three of us, the doctor, the engineer and I, strolled towards the Hastings and swung leisurely in through the wide door exactly as the fourth engine came to life. Without trying, we nearly always managed to get it right, the door slamming as the last engine started. Perhaps it was not altogether surprising ; for we had been doing it almost every two days in a succession of different countries since we left England a month before. We were to do it many times again.

Caracas was the half-way point in the series of courtesy visits which took our four Canberras of Bomber Command twenty-four thousand miles through South America and the Caribbean. In the beginning, the object of the expedition had been to pay our respects to the new President of the Republic of Chile at the ' Transmision del Mando ', in continuation of the custom established in 1948, when four Lincoln heavy bombers had visited Santiago to take the good wishes of Britain and the Royal Air Force to his predecessor when he came to power.

News of our intentions brought requests for a visit from many neighbouring countries, and since all countries in that hemisphere like to be thought good neighbours, in the end ten foreign countries and four British colonies in South America and the Caribbean received the Canberras. The crews would say that ' received ' is a poor word to describe what happened, and it would be less than civil if I did not say at once that we were treated with a lavishness long forgotten by modern Britons.

I did not think that South American hospitality, administered by a fresh team in each country every few days, would mix successfully with our servicing schedules, necessarily often beginning before dawn, but all the crews kept wide awake from start to finish and thoroughly enjoyed themselves as well. They were not exactly 'greeting the dawn with a glad shout' towards the end, but there was no failure of any sort.

There were plenty of official ceremonies, courtesy calls on Presidents, Ministers of Foreign Affairs and Chiefs of the Armed Forces, often attended by the Press; but crew conferences on matters such as the technique of high-altitude flying in the tropics and vital repairs to aircraft, held to the accompaniment of photographers' flashes and in the presence of reporters, were at first difficult. We sometimes longed for a comfortably storm-tossed battle-ship in which to conduct our domestic affairs between ports in the manner of the Royal Navy when they go visiting; but battleships cannot go to Bogota, so that was the end of the matter. Fortunately the gentlemen of South America are, by long tradition, model hosts, and we discovered that those of the Press are no exception. They therefore respected our wishes. In return we gave them the fullest possible latitude. We let them know everything we could, and to judge by the packing-case full of Press cuttings which arrived recently our confidence was not misplaced. The articles and news reports are nearly all from the front pages, and they are written with an appreciation and understanding of important features that can only come from keen and knowledgeable interest.

At Caracas we began to feel that we would, after all, succeed. We had made the preparations for the flight under conditions normal to the Royal Air Force. I mean that we were without a precedent to guide us. There was no manual in which we could turn up 'Tours, Jet, South America, Conduct of'. However, we had plenty of optimism, but not blind optimism by any means. While we could imagine what might lie ahead, we did not *know*, and neither did anyone else.

To obtain the best range, all jet aircraft must fly high, the Canberra above forty thousand feet. Yet less was known of the weather at high altitudes above the Andes or the South Atlantic, or anywhere on the route, than is known of the life of a mollusc a similar distance under the sea. What, if they existed at all, were the directions and intensities of the 'jet streams', those very rapid bursts of meteorological energy which go boring hundreds of miles through the upper air like blasts from the nozzle of a gigantic bellows? Again, what was the upper limit of the turbulent clouds of the inter-tropical front? The results we found were surprising but not dangerous.

The fuel performance was in question. At Dakar, on the brink of the seventeen-hundred mile breadth of the South Atlantic, the Avtur fuel pumped into the tanks of the aircraft would be at a high tropical temperature. When the aircraft climbed, the fuel would contract under the influence of the low air temperatures encountered at extreme height. Thus the extraordinary situation would be created in which fuel would be 'lost' without ever leaving the tanks. The volume would be reduced and the aircraft might run out of fuel before reaching land. Calculations can be made, of course, but calculations depend on exact temperature measurement; and the Canberras were to fly in hotter as well as colder conditions than ever before. Surprisingly, it is considerably colder at forty thousand feet above the equator than at the same height over the North or South Poles. A 'loss' of fuel to some extent could be foreseen, but the effect of these large and rapid changes of temperature on the performance of the fuel itself was not known with any certainty.

All sorts of unsolved problems such as these were in the background, and that is where they stayed until they were solved by experience. It was, after all, a purely pioneering flight. No jet aircraft had flown to those places before. High-altitude airfields, short airfields, tropical conditions and long-range navigation without radar aids were all normal hazards which had been overcome for many years by conventional aircraft, but for jets they were still a mystery. Also very much of a mystery to the young crews were the ways of diplomatic and governmental receptions in foreign capitals and life generally among the South Americans. They need not have had any doubts; they fitted themselves into the picture without any apparent effort at all and danced their way round the continent with excellent grace.

As I stood watching the Canberras take off from their base at Binbrook in Lincolnshire on that cold, wet October morning, bound for Gibraltar on the first stage of the journey, I could not help feeling that now, if ever, was a chance for the rising generation to prove itself and to balance the account a little with those wartime air and ground crews who, in a quiet way, as many 'old boys' do, had hinted that the school was not quite up to its former standard.

The Commander-in-Chief had come to see us off, and I could see him pointing out to one of the South American Air Attachés the badge painted on the fuselage of each of the Canberras. It was the squadron crest in the form of a fox's head with the motto 'Leads the Field'. Our foxes, I thought, will need all their cunning if they are to succeed in this chase through unfamiliar country.

The last Canberra disappeared into the drizzle and I was joined by the doctor and the engineer at the door of the Hastings. We climbed forward over the tangle of equipment firmly lashed to the floor of the large freight cabin, and settled into the seats we were to eat in, and doze and read and write in for the next seven weeks.

The seats were not uncomfortable, but there were certainly not to be any luxuries. A further notable point was that we were seated looking aft. As a practising pilot of some fifteen years' experience, now confronted with a twenty-four thousand mile tour as a passenger, I was not attracted by the idea of doing the whole journey facing the tail. Still, there was the comforting thought that in the most unlikely event of a forced landing or other sudden stoppage, it is less damaging to be restrained by the seat itself from top to bottom than by a small safety-strap across the abdomen.

Seated near the forward end of the freight compartment I could see, just above the top of the high-backed seats, the heads of the servicing crew showing ginger, light and dark, some ruffled and some, just in from starting the Canberras, glistening wet with the rain. We were all very cold in our thin khaki drill.

The deep hum of the four Hercules engines increased

and we trundled forward, the pilot guiding the aircraft along the twisting perimeter track to the take-off point by alternate bursts of engine. At 10 a.m. precisely we took off for Gibraltar, half an hour after the Canberras. Another Hastings, with the rest of the equipment and a small party of servicing men, had gone ahead on the previous day, and we intended to play 'leapfrog' with it so that there should always be some of us to meet the Canberras and, even more important, someone to see them off.

We flew to Selsey Bill and thence our journey was straight and uneventful, over the Bay of Biscay and the jagged brown highlands of Spain to Gibraltar.

There was the Rock, with the narrow runway jammed up against it, one end in the sea and the other in the harbour, more like a carrier's flight-deck than a landing-strip. One Canberra pilot had been deceived by it, and the treacherous mid-day air currents swirling round the Rock had caused him to finish up with steaming brakes and his nose over the harbour water. But now, as our Hastings lumbered in, the shadow of the Rock was beginning to creep across the runway and the air was calm. She sat down heavily and taxied back to park beside the four Canberras. They had landed in time for lunch ; we were just in time for a gin before dinner.

The following morning was marvellously clear until the intended time of departure. Then the sky grew dark, and an enormous cumulus cloud, which had been reported by the Met. to be working itself into a thunderous frenzy over Tangier, drifted across the Strait and dropped several thousand tons of water on Gibraltar. It was hardly possible to see across the runway but, through occasional breaks in the torrent of heavy rain, cloud

161

streamers could be seen writhing round the upper part of the Rock, making sudden vicious darts towards the ground and rising again with great speed. Such a display of force left little to the imagination of any pilot who might have been tempted to chance his luck. The prospect of a day's delay was dreadful, and the local experts were not prepared to say how long these violent conditions would last. To take off then would have been asking for trouble, so we sat down and waited. Within half an hour the sky to the south showed signs of a temporary clearance and that was enough. The crews dashed to their aircraft through the rain. In a matter of minutes the first Canberra was plunging down the partly flooded runway, throwing up a mass of water which thumped horribly on the undersides of the main planes and was immediately transformed into large clouds of steam by the intense heat from the jet pipes. The remainder followed, and the four were seen to be strung out at six- or seven-mile intervals, their small black shapes diminishing swiftly against the watery sky as they climbed away across the Strait. They were through the cloud and at forty thousand feet within a few minutes. The temperature outside the cockpits was, of course, arctic, and the pilots gingerly tried the rudder and elevator controls for signs of jamming. They were suspicious that some of the water shipped during the take-off might have lodged in the control mechanisms and be freezing them solid, a distinctly unpleasant prospect. But apart from a little stiffness there was no trouble. The cockpits, although heated to some extent, become very cold after a short time, and for the next three and a half hours the drenched crews shivered their way over the Sahara Desert at just over four hundred knots to Dakar, some 1,500 nautical miles distant.

In the jet era we must not now expect crews and passengers to recount the delights of their journeys in terms of the majestic mountains and famous buildings which have been so dear to air travellers for the last decade or so, any more than we would expect an assessment of the beds and hospitality in the inns between London and Canterbury on Chaucerian lines from a young man in a fast sports car on that road. From forty thousand feet the earth, seven and three-quarter miles below, is flat and colourless and, unless the aeroplane is banked, it cannot be seen at all by the pilot. There is nothing but the sky, the diamond-bright sun and the black shadows in the cockpit. Flight is mainly by instruments, and there is an almost complete absence of sensation. There is little noise, and it is so unchanging that there is an odd impression of complete silence. The pilot can easily believe that he has escaped into a fourth dimension, there to hang, relaxed and partly hypnotised, in a pleasant state of complete suspension entirely without movement, progressing neither in time nor in space. All is still. The hands of the mach. meter, fixed at nearly sonic speed, and the pointers of the altimeter showing the earth to be nearly eight miles beneath, cease to be the realities. They become trivial and unimportant until they suddenly start to move. The aeroplane is losing height and gaining speed. Something must be done, and so the spell is broken. A gentle backward pressure on the control column, a slight movement of the right thumb on the trimming button, and all is well. The aeroplane is again flying straight and level and at the correct speed and height.

Christopher Columbus would probably have had a good deal of difficulty in learning to fly a Canberra, but he would have taken to the navigation like a duck to water once he had become used to working in minutes instead of days. He would have found the principles of dead reckoning the same. The compass would be familiar to him. Sitting beside the navigator, just behind the pilot, he would easily have taken over the air plot and become a useful member of the three-man crew; for on this South American tour there were none of the radar aids on which the home-based Canberra relies, and the chief navigation instruments were the time-honoured ruler and dividers.

Besides carrying the normal magnetic compass, each Canberra was specially fitted with a 'radio compass'. To the purist this is not a compass at all, but merely a short-range radio set indicating on a compass card the direction of the station to which it is tuned. Using this, the pilot can fly towards his destination airfield if there is a radio transmitter there. The navigator can also obtain bearings from any radio transmitter there may be on the route. The range of reception is roughly only two hundred miles, or about twenty-five minutes' flying, and for homing and navigation its use is limited because it cannot indicate distances; and distances are of extreme importance when bringing a jet aeroplane down through cloud to heights where fuel consumption is so high that a too early descent may cause it to run out. There are similar difficulties if the descent is made too late.

In the Hastings we were moving along at about two

hundred knots, and for eight hours we saw nothing but sand and sea. But at last we reached Dakar, and as we lost height on the approach the air in the cabin became progressively hotter, and sweaters and coats were rapidly removed. I thought of the Canberra crews who had been drenched, then frozen, and then roasted as they flew low round the circuit at Dakar, the equatorial sun streaming through their clear plexiglass cockpit covers. So great had been the heat in the cockpits that the pilots said it was quite refreshing to get out into the cooler atmosphere of Dakar airfield, where even the coloured inhabitants were lolling about in the heat with wet towels round their necks.

As the Hastings lumbered round the airfield before landing we craned our necks to see if all four Canberras had arrived. This was the first long and desolate stretch of the route and we knew that difficulties of navigation, or with fuel or oxygen supplies, could have serious results. Only three Canberras could be counted on the tarmac. There was gloom indeed in the Hastings as we wondered who had failed to arrive and whether they were safe. And then, suddenly, the other was seen with its nose safely tucked up against the refuelling bowser which had obscured it from us until the last moment.

We reached the Hotel Croix du Sud after a fifteen-mile drive from the airfield. The Canberra crews were being entertained by the British Consul, but we were too late to change and make an excusably delayed entry. A few of us were cooling off over glasses of icy beer when the Squadron Commander came in from the cocktail party and told us we were expected to dine at the home of General of Brigade 'X' in fifteen minutes, and disappeared upstairs to his room. We followed suit and in ten minutes we had re-assembled, no longer cool, but clothed correctly in the blue trousers and short white jackets of tropical mess kit. We leapt into a car and sped off to enjoy an evening's entertainment which only a French host bent on pleasing his guests could produce.

In the morning the Canberras were inspected by French officers and colonial officials, and we were shown the Air Force base where among other things desert rescues are organised. It was very much like our Air-Sea Rescue service, except that the searching aircraft directed jeeps, camels and tracked vehicles instead of fast launches. That afternoon, and later in the stifling dining-room of the hotel that evening, we had many long and serious discussions about the coming flight across the South Atlantic. None of the pilots had flown modern jet aircraft in tropical conditions, and no information was available about operating the Canberra from tropical air-fields. It was to be the first jet crossing of the South Atlantic ever made, and the main causes of our pre-occupation, apart from the effects of high temperatures on fuel consumption, were the impossibility of getting really accurate forecast of the winds at forty thousand feet, and the lack of means of fixing position or measuring ground speed for the middle six hundred miles of the crossing. In the background was the loneliness of the South Atlantic. The North Atlantic, by comparison, seemed to be a paradise where weather ships, accurate forecasts, radio aids, and other such delights abounded.

Finally, a flight plan was adopted in which the pilots were to turn back if they had insufficient fuel to allow for a hunred-knot head-wind when entering the six-hundred-mile stretch where accurate navigation could not be done. This scheme was still a gamble, but it reduced the odds against them considerably. To the other diners the small group of Royal Air Force officers, in civilian clothes, quietly talking at a table in a corner of the dimly-lit restaurant must have been insignificant. In fact, a first-class display of leadership and scientific knowledge was going on. On the one hand was the technically brilliant pilot who displayed every possible aspect of the coming flight in terms such as fuel expansion rates, flight endurance, and navigational accuracy. He was carrying a tremendous load of detailed knowledge, and he also knew better than anybody what combinations of factors could send all four Canberras to the bottom of the South Atlantic. On the other hand was the Air Marshal, clearly understanding the difficulties as they were presented, balancing them against considerations of morale, logic, humanity and even politics. His thinking must also have included ideas about his own immediate future, for he was piloting one of the Canberras. A famous general once said that if after a visit you cannot leave your subordinates with the feeling that they have just had a glass of champagne you are not a leader. So many have to make do with cider, but what we had in Dakar was pure vintage, and we went to bed early feeling much better about the whole thing.

It was dark when my alarum-clock roused me. A few minutes later, after a quick *café complet*, we were on our way, and the sun rose out of the sea as we passed along the deserted coast road to the airfield. Some of the ground crews had been awake most of the night, topping up the aircraft tanks with cool Avtur fuel and performing detailed inspections before this momentous journey.

Half an hour before they were due to take off the

aircrews climbed into their cockpits and began their pre-flight drills of checking and testing. Then, with ten minutes to go, the engines were started and the first Canberra taxied forward, throwing clouds of thick desert dust over the other three as it turned towards the runway. The remaining Canberras followed, and we stood in the door of the Hastings to watch them take off. The Air Marshal, in 'Jet One'—that was the radio call-sign—ran his engines to seven thousand revs a minute and released the brakes. The thrust from the engines increased tremendously, and the aircraft accelerated down the runway with the shattering roar well known to anyone who has been to Farnborough or any jet station. The heavy fuel-laden aeroplane gained speed slowly and passed from sight behind the low scrub bordering the airfield. We held our breaths until finally it appeared again and rose, apparently at the very last moment, to climb on the seventeen-hundred mile journey over the ocean to Recife in Brazil. 'Jet Two' by this time was halfway down the runway, roaring loudly, but not, I thought, making good progress. An instant later there was complete silence as the pilot cut off the power. Our view was obstructed by the scrub and there was nothing to do but wait. Then we heard the rising shriek of the engines being opened up for taxi-ing and we knew that he had stopped successfully and was returning to the parking place. 'Jet Three' went through the same hair-raising performance and he too came taxi-ing back. 'Jet Four' took off. Two out of four. This was bad by any standards.

The engineer rapidly had the re-fuelling party standing by and the servicing crews were out of the Hastings by the time the non-starters had returned. We were ready for anything. One of them went straight back to the take-off point for another try. This time he was successful. The other came in for an engine test, and after a good deal of ground-running of the engines he too took off. Both these pilots reported loss of power during the first attempts at take-off, but no other abnormal features were observed. It was all something of a mystery at the time, but the cause was diagnosed later and a remedy was applied which prevented further unpleasantness.

All four Canberras were now airborne over the South Atlantic, flying with the sun. They were due at Recife about four hours later. In the Hastings, travelling at a mere two hundred knots and taking off soon after the last Canberra, we were to reach Recife six hours after it. And that is what happened.

The Canberra pilots did not see each other during the flight, but they all landed within the space of a few minutes, the fastest of them crossing in four hours and nineteen minutes. The Hastings too landed on time, but owing to a radio failure she could not communicate with Recife, and a B17 Flying Fortress, complete with airborne droppable lifeboat, took off to meet us and give assistance if necessary.

During their flight, done as usual at about forty thousand feet, the Canberra pilots had not encountered strong winds, and the effect of the high temperatures at Dakar on the fuel had been offset by a change in atmospheric conditions ; but they were surprised to see that quite heavy cumulus-type clouds had built up well above their normal flying height. In temperate latitudes the tropopause—beyond which clouds cannot form and the high-speed jet streams decrease in intensity—varies between thirty and forty thousand feet ; but over the

South Atlantic it was found to be between forty-five and fifty thousand feet, or even higher, and to see thick cloud at these heights for the first time was an unwelcome novelty. It was interesting to find that during the tour no weather forecast ever gave cloud above thirty thousand feet, and it was sometimes difficult to get the meteorologists to believe that cloud existed above this height. Perhaps it was not surprising ; for they had never spoken to anyone before who had been so high over their area, and it was stimulating to think that by flying at forty thousand feet on the whole route after leaving Gibraltar these Canberras were flying in airspace that had never been flown in before.

Two hundred miles out from the South American coast, that is about twenty-five minutes' flying, the Air Marshal was told on the radio from Recife that it was a Presidential election day for the State of Pernambuco and a public holiday. This news, while no doubt of the greatest importance, puzzled him, and it was not until he was within a few minutes of his destination that the remainder of the message came through. It asked him to make a few low passes over the beaches crowded with holiday makers. This he did, to their great delight.

During the two-day stop at Recife we were accommodated at the Brazilian air base in officers' quarters built round an open patio, and we were looked after extremely well. When our servicing tasks on the aircraft and our courtesy calls on the local authorities had been completed, we had some splendid bathing inside the reef. The long yellow beach is fringed with palms, and the Atlantic rollers, fetched in by the trade winds, break and roar endlessly on the lonely reef.

We were to be very glad of this quiet place on our

return five weeks later, but now we wanted to get on to see the long-imagined beaches of Rio de Janeiro, with their gay crowds and brilliant sun.

I went ahead in the Hastings and landed in a drizzle of rain at Galleão, the airport for Rio, the afternoon before the Canberras were due. After a descent by instruments the cloud-base had been just high enough for a visual final approach, so we saw nothing of Rio. The doctor and I were staying at the Embassy Residence, and the Air Attaché whirled us there in his car. The building is enormous. It is the largest British Embassy in the world, and was designed and constructed by the Office of Works for its purpose. Even in the rain its white façade looked magnificent. The interior was delightful ; and the very understanding Ambassador and his wife seemed quite unperturbed by our comings and goings at all hours.

It was still drizzling and gloomy in the morning, and when I went to Galleão to meet the Canberras there was low cloud and mist on the airfield. I thought, and rather hoped, they would not try to come, but at half-past ten we had a message to say that they had left Recife and were on their way. This caused a great stir. Soon most of the Diplomatic Corps of Rio, members of the Brazilian Air Force, people of the British community, and newspaper, radio and television men by the score were waiting in the rain beside the control tower. In the forefront was drawn up a Brazilian Air Force guard of honour with its band. The guard of honour was enormous, and must have comprised nearly the whole garrison. As I watched the rain sweeping across the airfield I was already thinking of some suitable way of telling this distinguished assembly that they had got wet for nothing. Then, through a break in the downpour, flying at about three hundred feet in and out of the low, fast-moving clouds, we saw a Canberra. It was soon enveloped by a fresh onset of rain, but a few minutes later, exactly at noon, which was the scheduled time, it landed perfectly and taxied to a position in front of the guard of honour. In a very short time the other three were neatly lined up beside it. The rain reduced itself to slight drizzle, and the Air Marshal, closing down his motors with one hand and putting on his gold-peaked cap with the other, jumped to the ground. The band played 'God Save the Queen' and the Brazilian National Anthem as he was met by the Ambassador and senior Brazilian Air Force officers. Still in flying overalls, he inspected the guard of honour and made a short speech on the Brazilian radio network, mentioning to the delight of his hearers the famous Brazilian aviator Santos Dumont, in whose memory a 'Wings Week' was being held. There followed at once a Press conference, consisting of all the crews and about seventy journalists, some of whom had come from other parts of Brazil for the occasion and meant to have their money's worth. Finally, the conference broke up and the crews went to lunch and then on to the hotels on the famous Copacabana beach in Rio where they were to stay. That evening there was a cocktail party at the Embassy for the British Officers and airmen, attended by most of the Diplomatic Corps of Rio, Brazilian Air Force Generals and leaders of aviation, five hundred guests in all.

Later most of us were taken off to see the bright lights of the town by friends we had made at the party. In true Rio tradition, few were in bed before dawn. It was a dawn which amply made up for the watery welcome of the previous day, and when the crews went out to the airfield to prepare for the flying exhibitions they were to give, the sun was blazing. Later, as they skimmed low along the crowded beaches and over the airfield they saw the Sugar Loaf, the Corcovado and other peaks round Rio standing out with startling clarity, and remembered how close they must have come to them in the cloud the day before.

The modern city of São Paulo is two hundred miles inland from Rio. It is almost as large, and its inhabitants consider it to be more go-ahead and up to date. They wanted to see the Canberras, and when it became known that there was a chance of doing so a crowd started to gather on the Campo de Marte at eight in the morning. When the low-flying Canberras went over at eleven-thirty the crowd had grown to about six thousand and was causing the most terrific traffic jam São Paulo had seen for years.

An urubu, a type of Brazilian vulture, also low flying over São Paulo, failed to take avoiding action in time and collided with one of the Canberras, shattering the plexiglass nose. The crew, and a Brazilian Air Force officer who was flying as a passenger, were lucky to escape without being injured, and the pilot brought the aircraft straight back to Rio to land without further trouble. The broken nose was replaced by a new one flown out from England within a few days, but the urubu was beyond repair.

Montevideo was our next stop, and the coolness was invigorating. The one and a half days there were fully occupied with official visits, receptions and flying demonstrations, and the final gesture was a low-level fly-past by

173

the Canberras in formation. Then they set course for the Argentine capital, a hundred and thirty miles away.

To the Canberra crews skimming at four hundred knots up the Rio de la Plata, the ships ploughing their way slowly through those grey waters seemed like stationary large-scale models with cotton wool bow waves. A small movement of the control column was sufficient to gain the thousand feet necessary to surmount the hills round Buenos Aires, and a few seconds later the aircraft were slanting down across the crowded Ministro Pistarini airfield in tight formation. The apparently silent approach, the impression of tremendous speed, and then the devasting roar left behind by the six Avon jet engines as the flight climbed rapidly into the distance made an immediate appeal to the dramatic sense of the Argentinos. They gasped and then cheered with great fervour. They had heard on the loudspeakers a few minutes before a message in Spanish which the formation leader had sent to the President of the Republic. The radio operator in the leading aircraft had somehow managed to get in touch with Buenos Aires in the short time at his disposal and sent the signal: 'The Royal Air Force, through the medium of No. 12 Squadron, sends greetings to His Excellency General Juan Domingo Peron the President of the Argentine Nation.' The crews received a warm welcome. So did the Air Marshal when he visited President Peron that morning at the Casa de Gobierno. With the British Ambassador and a number of government Ministers and high military officers, he went in and sat at the large polished table in the President's reception room. Upon it was a replica of the equestrian statue of the Liberator, General San Martin, and on the walls among the flags and pennants were paintings of past heroes of the Republic. With his Minister of Foreign Affairs on his right and the Air Marshal on his left, the President sat smiling his famous smile, and by the time the coffee and cigarettes were served the party was cheerfully discussing aviation and submitting to the flashes of the official photographer.

Another round of receptions and parties began. There were late nights, and early rising for servicing and re-fuelling. The circus routine of arriving at midday, working in the afternoon, demonstrating the aircraft the next day and off again in the morning was followed also at Buenos Aires. For the demonstration a crowd of cup final proportions had assembled at the airport in the brilliant sunshine. One Canberra was put through its paces for the benefit of the President watching from a balcony of the Casa Rosada, the Pink House ; another gave short flights to the Commander-in-Chief of the Argentine Air Force and his senior officers, and a third gave a flying display over the airfield. On the morning of the departure Argentine Air Force officers and Embassy officials braved the cold and the wet to say goodbye. The clouds were down to less than three hundred feet and getting worse. Reports from the destination, Santiago de Chile on the other side of the Andes, were brief and out of date. In these conditions the Canberras took off, and as the undercarriage of the last one left the runway and tucked itself up under the wings, the pilot, already on instruments, heard on the radio the unpleasant news that civil airline operations *en route* had been cancelled owing to bad weather. The Canberras climbed up through the murk and were shortly flying at forty thousand feet in clear air with an unbroken carpet of cloud beneath them. Soon the crews saw the snowy peaks of the Andes far below, dwarfed by the altitude, projecting through the clouds, and they realised why normal propeller-driven aircraft, incapable of doing more than thread their bumpy way through the passes, found them such a formidable barrier. Then the clouds thinned, and when they landed at the airport of Los Cerrillos in Santiago the air was crystal clear, giving unlimited visibility.

The wonderfully clean and refreshing air enjoyed in this part of Chile is due partly to the nearness of the Andes. The twenty-four thousand foot giant Aconcagua is less than seventy miles away, and within thirty miles of Santiago there is excellent ski-ing.

When the Canberras arrived the sun was almost painfully bright, the light striking up from the concrete surfaces with surprising intensity. Their reception, too, was rather surprising. A large crowd of men, women and children had taken advantage of a holiday granted to celebrate the coming inauguration of the new President to visit the airport. An instant after the Canberras had come to a standstill the crowd broke the barriers and surged forward to surround them. It was only with difficulty that the doors could be opened, but finally the Air Marshal was able to meet the Chilean Commander-in-Chief and inspect the guard of honour in their German-type helmets and uniforms before being whisked away to the Embassy. Before he went, a middle-aged man in civilian clothes approached with his arms out-stretched, saying " Do you recognise me?" This was most unexpected, but the Air Marshal placed him accurately as a Chilean officer to whom he had given flying instruction in England some twenty-five years

previously. He had retired from the Chilean Air Force
as a Brigadier-General.

When the senior officers had departed the fun began.
In the early days of flying one of the occupational hazards
was the dear old lady with the brolly who used to jab it
through the delicate fabric of the rudder or other con-
venient surface to prove some point of aircraft design
which had been vexing her young relatives. Multiply
this situation by several hundreds, put it into a foreign
language and you have an idea of the scene at Los
Cerrillos airfield. The noise was terrific. The young
police-guards sportingly made backs for the members of
the public to lift themselves to gaze into the dark interiors
of the jet pipes in return for similar services when their
own turn came. The whole affair was, to quote the
evening paper, 'a most affectionate welcome'. Nothing
was broken and when, again to quote, 'their anticipation
had been satisfied', the crowd allowed itself, with much
good humoured leg-pulling, to be herded gradually back
by a dozen or so British airmen in open order, carrying
between them a long rope.

Santiago was full to overflowing with foreign visitors
for the 'Transmision del Mando' of General Carlos
Ibañez del Campo, G.B.E. The ceremony took place
two days after our arrival, and in the afternoon there was
a grand military parade in the great Parque Cousiño at
which the new President reviewed his forces. For two
hours in the glorious sunshine troops marched past,
watched by a hundred and fifty thousand Chilenos and
foreign visitors, including Mrs Roosevelt, who was repre-
senting the United States. Units of the Chilean Army
goose-stepped past, a large number of ski troops padded
by in their thick boots and white clothing with their skis

over their shoulders, and many squadrons of superbly trained cavalry and batteries of horse artillery thundered across the arena at full gallop. Then, among the visiting troops, came a solid square of British sailors from the cruiser *Sheffield*, marching perfectly and preceded by their no-less precise Royal Marine band. Towards the end of the day the Fuerza Aerea de Chile flew over in formations of Thunderbolts, Mitchells and Harvards, fighters, bombers and trainers of the late war, followed at a few seconds' interval by our three Canberras which zipped across the arena in close formation like three flashes of blue lightning, leaving the roar and rumble of their engines mingling with the voices of the amazed crowd.

On the next day the demonstration flights were made. One Canberra burst a tyre while landing, but the pilot managed to keep the aeroplane on the runway. The servicing crews unloaded a new tyre from the freight cabin of the Hastings, fitted it to the Canberra, and it was flying again in less than twenty minutes.

The ceremonial visit to Chile was over, and the headline which announced ' Mrs Roosevelt and the Canberras leave today ' summed it all up neatly. There now remained a high-speed dash through ten more countries, and then home. The next stop was Lima, Peru.

I had gone ahead in the Hastings the previous day, arriving at Lima after a ten-hour flight up the Pacific coast with the Andes towering to starboard the whole way. All was ready for the Canberras the next morning, and a little after noon we saw them land after breaking through the layer of cloud which hangs over Lima for most of the year. The wind on the airfield was hardly noticeable, but at forty thousand feet over Lima a gale of about a hundred and seventy knots was raging and the Canberras were affected by it throughout the flight from Santiago. These high-speed winds, or jet streams, do not buffet an aircraft as one might expect after experience with gales on the ground. The results are unnoticeable, yet an aircraft can be swept smoothly many hundreds of miles off its intended track if the navigator is not wide awake and cannot get the bearings and fixes he requires.

At Lima all four Canberras were together again, and they performed the now familiar two-day circus routine. Next same Bogota, the Colombian capital tucked away in a natural bowl eight thousand feet up in the Andes. They landed at the airfield called Techo, the ceiling, and then went on to Maiquetia, a great airfield on the Venezuelan coast which serves Caracas. There the Minister of Defence, wisely avoiding the twenty-six mile road through the mountains, came down and landed beside the Canberras in his helicopter for a twenty-minute tour of inspection. He was particularly interested, because he was adding a squadron of Canberras to his Air Force to take their places beside the British Vampires already in service.

Next came the first British Colony on the route, British Honduras, on the western edge of the Caribbean. The stay in Belize was less exacting than at the previous ports of call, and the crews were able to relax a little and feel at home. The chief delights of Belize are fishing for tarpon, one of the toughest of big-game fish, and the sailing and bathing to be had in the clear, calm waters round the cays. The cays are delightful little coral islands several miles off the coast, bearing such solid British names as St George's Cay, English Cay, and

179

Sergeant's Cay. Sergeant's Cay is just big enough to hold a small house, a garden, a couple of palm-trees and no more.

From the tropical heat of Belize the flight went to the enormous airfield of Mexico City, which is over seven thousand feet up. They flew in over the snow-capped peaks of Popocatepetl and Ixtlaccihuatl, ' the smoking mountain ' and ' the white lady ', which overlook the city. Popo is a typical cone-shaped volcano and Ixtla, when viewed from the city, gives a remarkably lifelike impression of a woman reclining on her back with a white shroud over her. In the Aztec legend Prince Popo is keeping vigil over his dead princess.

The two bands on the runway played the Mexican and British National Anthems in quick succession, and then competed with each other by playing different tunes simultaneously. The inspection of the guard of honour over, the Air Marshal and his party were driven to the enormous Ministry of Defence buildings on the outskirts of the city, and were presented with wings and certificates of honourable mention by the General Commanding the Fuerza Aerea Mexicana. This was the first time Mexico had made such a gesture to a foreign mission. Wreath-laying at the monument to the Heroes of the Republic was followed by official receptions. After the demonstration flights at the airfield and over the city, one Mexican gentleman was heard to say that the Canberras reminded him of some Mexican revolutions because they appeared with a great noise and faded away rapidly without leaving any noticeable effect.

Coming back across the Caribbean the Canberras landed at sea level again at Havana, the Cuban capital.

They stayed long enough to be inspected by the President of the Republic and to give the Minister for Defence a quick flight, and then they were off again for Kingston, Jamaica. The furious pace of the tour was now beginning to tell, and everyone was extremely tired and glad to arrive in Jamaica, where a four-day sojourn had been arranged for leisure and rest. After the necessary servicing work had been done, there were in reality only two days left for swimming and sunbathing on those wonderful beaches. Much refreshed nevertheless, the party now flew over Haiti to Ciudad Trujillo, capital of the Dominican Republic. After our demonstrations there, the official task of the mission was accomplished. The flight was now free, according to its instructions, to return by the quickest means.

The United States bomber crews used to say, " Going to the target you're flying for Uncle Sam. Coming back you're flying for yourself." The Canberra crews were now flying for themselves, and when they reached Port of Spain in Trinidad they were in a gay mood ; and Trinidad was just the place for gaiety. As they swept over the town a little confusion was caused by some coloured gentlemen falling to their knees in the street and declaring that the end of the world was at hand. Otherwise everything was rosy, from the luxury of an air-conditioned hotel on the airfield—a service which no other place on the route could equal—to the dances and parties where the cheerful and brightly-costumed Trinidadians performed their wonderfully rhythmic dances, and sang calypsos about the Canberras and their crews to the music of the curious ' steel bands '. Their instruments are simply suitably tempered oil-drums, and produce the most beautifully pure notes imaginable. Before leaving for Belem, twelve hundred miles to the south on one of the mouths of the Amazon, a Canberra took advantage of a spare forty minutes to fly out to the island of Barbados, a round trip of about three hundred miles.

On the way to Belem, the Canberras came down from their cruising height of forty thousand feet to give a display for the inhabitants of Georgetown, British Guiana, by flying at water level up and down the river for about twenty minutes. There was a slight hold-up at Belem. One Canberra was discovered to have a leaking fuel pipe. A quick repair was done and it took off about forty minutes after the other three, covering the distance of a thousand miles between the mouth of the Amazon and Recife, over very lonely and partially unexplored country, in just under two hours.

The tour of South America and the Caribbean had now gone full circle, and back again at Recife preparations were made for the west to east crossing of the Atlantic to Dakar. Owing to more favourable winds the time for this crossing beat the outward-bound time by thirty minutes, the seventeen-hundred-odd miles being covered in three hours forty-nine minutes. Retracing their track of five weeks ago, the Canberras crossed the Sahara and reached Gibraltar exactly on the day scheduled, as indeed they had done at all their ports of call. Nobody now doubted that we would reach England on time. A signal had arrived stating that the Secretary of State for Air, the Commander-in-Chief, the B.B.C. television and sound services, and the Press were to be at the Canberras' base at Binbrook for the landing. Then, after almost twenty-four thousand miles of continuous good weather, with a few notable exceptions, Britain produced widespread fog and low cloud.

We all wanted to be back together so that the ground crews and the Hastings crews could take part in whatever welcome was awaiting us, and from the signal it looked pretty high-class. The Hastings, with its load of now empty oxygen cylinders, the ground crews, a couple of parrots, an unidentified raincoat, and other sundries that included the tired doctor, engineer and me, took off from Gibraltar before dawn while the Canberra crews slept on. They would leave four hours later and still arrive with us.

Over France we received a radio instruction not to land at Binbrook because it, and most of England except the West Country, was weather bound. The air above France was clear, and the frost on the fields below sparkled in the morning sun ; but when we crossed the Channel a pall of low black clouds could be seen hanging over England. It was almost unbelievable that our homecoming was not, so to speak, to be at home. We therefore stood on for Binbrook, just in case the weather lifted, and to make sure that if it did the Canberras would not steal a march on us. Then, flying in cloud over the Midlands, we heard the Canberras accepting their diversion to St Eval. They were at forty thousand feet somewhere near Paris. We came round in a steep turn and went full-out to beat the Canberras to the West Country. We failed by a quarter of an hour. We were just in time to enter the operations room to hear the Commander-in-Chief give his speech of welcome and read out messages of congratulation from the Secretary of State for Air and the Foreign Secretary. The sudden switch to St Eval and the terrible flying weather had made it impossible for the Secretary of State, the television people and others to meet us, but the Commander-in-Chief and a number of newspaper correspondents had somehow managed to get through.

This was the homecoming. It was restful even to feel tired at St Eval, secure in the knowledge that soon, as soon as I liked, I could go to bed, have dinner, or have a pint of bitter first, just as I felt. There was no mad rush from the airfield to yet another marathon of receptions and late parties. And above all, I could sleep until I awoke. There was no crackling telephone in the dark before dawn to say, "*Las cinco menos cuarto señor, muy buenos dias!*" and no agonising waits for the late-coming taxi whose failure to arrive might throw the whole tour out of gear. There would be no doubts, no worries, and no dirt in the fuel tomorrow. Calm English voices would guide us safely home to Binbrook over the beloved patchwork quilt of woods and fields that is England, and it would feel good to be home to stay. England was the best place in the world just then, but there is a nomadic streak in most of us in the Royal Air Force and the urge to see new sights and do new things is strong. It is small wonder then that the raincoat, afterwards identified, found its way back to its owner, a British Colonial Governor in the Caribbean, by way of Singapore.

['Maga' January 1954.

12

THE AIR RACE
Brian Haimes

I suppose that the first competition ever devised by man was some form of race. As like as not the earliest kind developed into straightforward pursuit and the prize was simply survival. Since those less complicated days, a good deal of ingenuity has gone into the framing of rules for racing, particularly the more bizarre sort. The 'Daily Mail' Air Race last summer was one of these: and although it was called an Air Race and was planned to commemorate the fiftieth anniversary of M. Blériot's Channel crossing, the real fun was not in the air, but before we took to the air at all, and after we landed on the other side. There was a lot about it in the Press, now all but forgotten, like any other nine-day wonder; but it was worth a more permanent record—our team thought so anyway—and here is the story.

The rules said that attempts had to be made between sunrise and sunset, and the route was from the Marble Arch to the Arc de Triomphe, or *vice versa*. I had thought of a helicopter from Marble Arch to Biggin Hill and a two-seater jet from there to France, but I had no control over any such aircraft, and it was obvious that people who had were probably going to use them themselves.

I had spoken to Douglas Bader about it and he was scornful about jets. Given permission to take off from Hyde Park and land in the Bois de Boulogne, he reckoned one would have a good chance of winning in a little Miles Gemini. But the rules said that competitors had to conform to the prevailing laws of both countries. It had begun to look as if the whole thing would become an exercise in bureaucracy—a tour round the various Ministries to see what one could get away with.

I rather lost interest, until Allen Wheeler happened to mention one day that he was hoping to organise an entry for his wife Barbara, which involved a group of people in BEA, and also de Havillands, who might lend us a Comet.

" If you like," he said, " I'll ask them to find a place for you. But I don't think there is any future in helicopters, their forward speeds are so low ; so I've got a scheme to use a London bus and a diesel train to Northolt. Far the quickest way. I'm just going to try and sell my plan to the BEA people in return for three places on a Comet. After that I must drop out, because I'm a steward in the race and I can't really get involved."

Now, my friend Allen Wheeler is a very aeronautical sort of chap: he served thirty years in the Air Force and ended up as an Air Commodore after an outstanding career as a test pilot. The interesting thing is that where other people retire and look after their roses Allen keeps on. He advises on aeroplanes, he tests aeroplanes, he uses an aeroplane for personal transport and owns several others. He even collects antique aeroplanes as other people collect paintings. So when he talked about diesels and buses, I knew he must have been thinking that part out pretty deeply.

" I'll let you know how I get on," said Wheeler, and that same afternoon he called back to say that all was arranged.

Three weeks later, we were standing in the sunshine waiting to go.

By then there had been about ninety attempts, and the competition from Royal Air Force and Royal Navy teams was really tough. With all their men and all their jet fighters to call on they were making the trip in about forty-three minutes. We could not hope to beat that, so we obviously could not win the first prize of £5,000 ; but we had hopes of winning the special prize of £1,000 for the most praiseworthy effort.

We stood in line by the time-clock, sweating gently under the hot sun and holding our time-cards in trembling hands. A ' Daily Mail ' man with a loud-hailer was talking to a crowd of two or three thousand people while lines of Sunday traffic rolled past through Hyde Park.

" In five minutes' time, ladies and gentlemen, the BEA-line Syndicate will begin their attempt to win the Blériot Anniversary race to Paris. The team consists of two ladies and eleven gentlemen. They will travel by London bus, British Railways diesel train, de Havilland Comet 4B, and Paris taxi."

We kidded ourselves we were just doing this for laughs, but there was a good deal of deadly earnestness. So much work had gone into the organisation and there were so many volunteers helping us that we had to do our best or die in the attempt.

" The time is 12.02. Four minutes to go," said Peter

Pinfield, the team captain, standing at the side of the line like an anxious schoolmaster. In front of me, No. 1, was Edwin Whitfield, BEA Traffic Director. As soon as he had punched his race-card in the time-clock it was my job to punch mine and get out, leaving the way clear for Bill Simpson, BEA's chief of Public Relations, and the rest of the syndicate lined up behind.

" Attention, please," said Peter with a rather pleading note in his voice. " Remember we've changed our exit route since the last rehearsal. We are not now going through the Park gates. When you've stamped your card, turn left, run past the caravans and go out through the narrow footpath leading to the ladies' lavatory. The bus is parked there, well past the traffic-lights."

" Mind you don't go down the wrong path," said Bill Simpson threateningly.

" Three minutes to go," said the timekeeper.

There were photographers darting about.

" Can we have you stamping your card, please?"

" Everybody in line again, please, we'll take a group."

Mrs Scott-Hill, the wife of another member of the team, appeared with a wicked-looking pair of scissors, probably the ones she had used to cut the crimson carnations worn by each male member of the team. She carefully clipped the corners off my race-card so that it would go into the time-clock easily.

" Two minutes."

I buttoned up all three buttons on my jacket. Not pretty but better than having it flapping. Every pocket had been carefully emptied of papers and loose change. Passport, embarkation card and competitor's F.A.I. licence in the left-hand pocket, race-card in the inside pocket. It was vital not to lose that.

" One minute."

Somewhere among the brightly-coloured mass of people in summer frocks and sports shirt were my wife and family. They thought it was screamingly funny to see father dashing round in the hot sun. Why, the poor old chap had never been known to move any faster than a slow trot. They little knew that he still cherished eighteen-year-old memories of star performances over obstacle courses in India.

The closer the race the more like an obstacle course it got, but the organisation was very detailed and careful. Each of us knew exactly where to sit in our bus, what order to get off in and where to go on the train.

" Thirty seconds," said the timekeeper, and there were still several photographers and friends standing round us chatting.

" Stand away, please," said Peter. Positively anguished this time. " Stand *away*."

" Only harsh word he ever said," murmured Whitfield.

" Ten seconds."

" Five seconds. Four. Three. Two. One."

Edwin Whitfield jumped as if he was shot, banged down the knob on the time-clock, snatched his card and was gone. With both hands I fed my card carefully into the slot. I was trying to be quick, but I was determined not to fluff it, and it seemed to take a tremendous time. Then I was off, in a sharp left turn, streaking along, completely oblivious of everything but the double line of fencing leading to the path through the trees.

Then, terrible anticlimax. A voice from behind shouted, " Your card's not stamped." I felt dreadful. Without a time stamp the entry was useless. I came to a complete and confused halt and said one of those four-lettered military words which seem so suitable to these occasions. I thought I muttered to myself, but delighted giggles from somewhere behind suggested it may have been a fairly loud mutter. Simultaneously I looked at the card. Large as life there was the stamp 12.06.02. Everything was fine. Oh, clot. Idiot. Fool. Why did he shout a thing like that?

Off again, running like a mad thing. Right-turn into the narrow-railed path between the trees and bushes. I was going too fast for that and skidded a bit. On again, then a left turn. This time I could not turn. Jump for the stone base of the railings, hit it with the right foot, turn left on the rebound and out into the sunshine. Across the pavement there was only a narrow path, lined by scores of tightly-packed people, just a blur of colours and pink faces. And there was our secret weapon—the London Transport omnibus. Two decks and clumsy, but with a first-class power-to-weight ratio and a very low centre of gravity. I hit the platform immediately behind Edwin Whitfield, practically knocked him over, and then fell into my seat, gasping for breath, sweating and incapable. The motor was roaring and the others came tumbling aboard, Bill Simpson, Len Leaver, Barbara Wheeler. Peter Pinfield appeared from nowhere and banged the bell. Roy Laver and Jimmy James popped up out of a mass of people. The bus-driver was revving his engine hard, Peter punched the bell again and the bus began to move. Peter Brooks appeared, running desperately, leaped for the step and we were off down the Bayswater Road heading for Paddington at about fifty miles an hour.

The difficulties in this section were sharp corners, other traffic which neither knew nor cared about us, and traffic-lights. The first bend was about two hundred yards ahead, sharp right, and a car was coming the other way. Bill Eldridge, the bus-driver, was quite ruthless and went for the corner at forty-five degrees. I caught a glimpse of the unfortunate car-driver screeching to a startling halt and then we were into the corner and Eldridge was bent over his wheel, heaving and heaving to the right to miss a yellow-and-black striped signpost on the pavement. It slid past the nearside wing and we were off again up Hyde Park Street heading for the traffic-lights which had held us up twice in rehearsals. The bus was full of the breathless gabble of people telling one another what hazards and difficulties they had overcome in the killing rush from the time-clock. Dick Chadwick of BEA's Route Facilities Department had his ever-present mental slide-rule going and was comparing figures with Len Leaver, the Transport Manager. It looked as if the whole team of thirteen had got through the time-card punching in twenty-seven seconds.

" The traffic-lights are green," said someone delightedly. There was a chorus of " Good show!" Len Leaver said, " That was Fred. Good old Fred." As we rocked round the left turn at the lights I saw briefly the back of a man in a brown suit and trilby hat stepping off the road onto the pavement. Fred, presumably. Every line of him radiated satisfaction at a job well done. Probably the poor man had been jumping up and down on the rubber road-pads for the last five minutes to keep the lights green.

Round we went, hard right again with the top of the bus swaying tremendously to the left. There was a grey Vauxhall Velox behind us now hooting furiously. As he was apparently much incensed at our mad career and we were not terribly sympathetic, someone made Sir Winston Churchill's victory sign which, in the right circumstances, has suitably rude connotations. Poor misunderstood fellow! It turned out later he had been specifically asked to follow us making all this noise because the bus-driver did not dare take his hands off the wheel long enough to punch the horn.

"Right. Action stations for getting off the bus," Peter Pinfield called out, and we lined up in our appropriate positions behind him, hanging on to anything we could see. The bus went down the ramp into Paddington still doing about fifty and Eldridge stood on the brakes. It was a first-class dead stop and we were off, tearing through the booking hall for our hired diesel train.

There it was, with three doors open, exactly as arranged. Right-hand door for me, the orders said, and here I was practically climbing up Peter Pinfield's back. Impossible to get round in front of him and the way to the right was blocked by the roof pillars. Very frustrating. But the platform was wide open. Peter steamed for his middle door, the way was clear and I got round him. I was vaguely aware of barriers and crowds of people. Then through the open door, without touching the floor or sides, and collapse on the farthest seat. Ian Scott-Hill came hustling red-faced through the middle door, bowler hat, carnation and all. The others were jumping and falling all over the place and then the doors slammed and we were off for Ruislip Gardens station and Northolt Airport.

At last, a chance for a bit of a rest. Barbara Wheeler was slumped opposite me fanning herself, gasping and distinctly dishevelled. Mary Willis was nursing a gash on her knee which had ruined a good pair of nylons. Ian

Scott-Hill looked as if he would never last out. The gabble of voices was on again and Peter Brooks and Dick Chadwick were busy comparing times.

"Two and a half minutes from Marble Arch to Paddington," they said in tones of awe. "The driver deserves a medal."

We all agreed wholeheartedly. The schedule allowed four minutes for that bit and we thought that was tight. If only the train-driver could make up a bit on his time-table we stood a good chance of getting to the Arc de Triomphe within the hour. Our original rather fat schedule of seventy-eight minutes had been cut down in rehearsal to sixty-nine, then to sixty-four, and I was determined that if we did not break the hour it would not be my fault. We knew we had no chance of beating those wonderful individual times of forty to forty-three minutes that were being put up by the Service entries and by Eric Rylands, using Hunters and Scimitars. Still, sixty minutes would be very close to the fifty-seven minutes achieved by the Special Air Service entry, and we thought that would be pretty good for two ladies and eleven elderly gentlemen.

I went up front to see how we were doing. The white-haired driver was crouched over his controls, hand on the throttle, the speedometer needle flickering round seventy miles an hour. The front of the single-coach train was nodding and swaying and the line of track stretched perfectly straight ahead to Ruislip eight or nine miles away. A train control-bar appeared between the tracks, flicked against the bottom of the train and a bell rang to indicate that the signal was open.

"How far to Ruislip?"

"Not far now. Past the next station there's a signal-box and then we go straight into the platform."

It was a disused platform, a rather rickety wooden affair, old, black with dirt and without any overhead shelter. The exit was rather complicated and I decided that this was where Haimes made his great effort. The operational orders called for myself, Peter Pinfield and Edwin Whitfield to open the doors and get out at a given signal. However, wide experience of suburban commuting persuaded me that I could be out and away down the steps before anyone else, provided I did not wait. Obviously a case for breaking the rules.

" No, look," I said to Barbara Wheeler, " I'm not waiting for the signal. I'll open the door before we reach the platform and jump before the train stops. There's a pretty fair wind pressure against this door and it'll bounce right back on you, so have your hand out to stop it."

She nodded, and Jimmy James, number three out of that door, said he would reach out to hold it too. As there is about six feet four inches of him, it seemed a fair arrangement, and I edged the door open a little. There were several posts supporting overhead cables very close to the line, so it seemed a good idea not to open it farther.

" Action stations," said Peter Pinfield.

Everybody got up and I pushed my door open against the wind and held it against the side of the train, still in my seat, one foot on the step. Barbara Wheeler was clearly convinced I was going flat on my face and held on to my coat-tails firmly. Vanity was slightly wounded, but it seemed churlish to object.

The train began to slow, the deceleration forced us all forwards and then, just before we reached the platform, the train whipped through a gentle S-bend. It was very slight but completely unforeseen. Those who were on their feet were swiftly deposited all over the compartment. We were lucky. Being still in our seats it made no difference and out I went, first onto the platform, pounding for the stairs leading down to the street. One achieves a peculiar mental state in a situation like this, when the objective is visible just ahead and the mind is leaping to it but the feet just won't go any faster. It's a sort of suspended animation—one seems to be absolutely static, making no progress at all. But no time to think about that. The steps went steeply down through a dark tunnel and now I seemed to have too many feet. In rehearsal, the man behind me had gone down this dreadful slope on the seat of his pants. Now there was the added stimulus of twelve people pounding behind. Including Len Leaver who weighs about fifteen stone.

At the bottom, skid to the right and head for a narrow door in a wooden partition. Was it open? Yes, it was. Thank heavens for organisation. Through the door, thirty feet along a concrete passage, down four steps in one leap, grab a metal stanchion to turn left round the corner, a glimpse of a policeman looking placid and amused, then out into the sunshine and there was Mac McKerrow's smooth Vauxhall Velox with all its doors open, only thirty yards away. A crew bus behind it with the doors taken off. Good Lord, what a lot of people. Crowds of them. Into the car, scraping my shin on the door edge, then collapse again, hot and sweaty with a bruised leg and my hands covered in dirt and tar from various things used as pivots for cornering.

Pinfield, Whitfield and Simpson arrived with three separate crashes and the car was off with a jerk and a skid of wheels on gravel, horn blaring and driver's arm stuck out for the sharp turn into Northolt Aerodrome. Why nearly all the turns had to be right-angles I shall never know. The path beyond the gate had only one bad bend, to the left, but there was a building hard up against it on the left and then halfway round was a tree hard up against the other side. It was completely blind, and during the planning Ian Scott-Hill had looked at the tree speculatively. Before he had time to open his mouth the otherwise co-operative Station Commander remarked drily, " I am *not* cutting down any trees."

Beyond the green shade of the trees the bare airfield opened suddenly in the sunlight and there was our Comet shining silver on the runway with all four engines screaming. The grass banks at the side of the field seemed to have flowered overnight where hundreds of people had turned out to watch the show. McKerrow probably ruined a good set of tyres skidding to a stop, and willing hands swung the doors open wide. My private plan to be first up the steps was frustrated ; for I had agreed with Edwin Whitfield that he could have my front seat in the car to take a ciné film, and I was jammed in the comfortable seats at the back between Bill Simpson and Peter Pinfield. Bill was rather slow getting out. It must have taken him at least a second and a half. I was beginning to fume, forgetting that he had no hands as a result of being shot down during the war. Still, with a bit of a heave from behind he popped out like a cork from a bottle and away we all went up the stairs to the crew door. I wondered how Ian Scott-Hill would get on, steering his bowler hat past the air-intakes.

The crew car behind, despite the efforts of Gordon Weston, an absolutely intrepid driver, had been rather slower, having had to load nine people, but after a few

seconds' pause its passengers came bounding up the steps
and crowding into the aisle of the Comet. Jimmy James,
last man in, had the responsibility of closing the door,
and I swear we were rolling before the door was shut.
By now, everybody knows that the Comet literally goes
up like a lift and can easily be at two thousand feet over
the end of any reasonable take-off runway. The snag
with this one was that it faced the wrong way and we
could lose a lot of time in a dignified take-off. I was
delighted when Peter Bugge hauled over in a steep turn
as soon as we were safely clear.

Beneath the starboard wing was London Airport like
something in an air-survey photograph, the country round
it all light brown in a dusty haze after nearly a month
without rain. There was another airfield farther south
with a single runway. Probably Vickers at Weybridge or
Wisley.

Our attention was diverted by Peggy Sanders, the
stewardess, who was bringing round lunch-trays. Within
the syndicate there had been two schools of thought,
those who were all for a mad dash and those who felt the
operation should be as like a normal air-line operation as
possible. For the moment the 'normal' element was
obviously in the ascendant, although practically no one
felt like eating. However, smoked salmon, caviare,
chicken and ham, fresh fruit-salad and champagne are
difficult to refuse. Although my conscience pricked me,
I quelled it with the thought that I needed the meat for
energy and the champagne to inculcate the proper
couldn't-care-less attitude required for the occasion. I
felt, too, that the dash from Le Bourget into Paris by taxi
might be best experienced through a slightly anæsthetic

haze of alcohol. Unhappily, there was not nearly enough. Not because of a misplaced sense of economy, but because there was not time. The Comet was rolling at Northolt at 12.24 plus a few seconds and it was scheduled to land at 12.52. We crossed the English coast at about 12.35 and I was still scooping up fruit-salad when the stewardess began collecting the trays. Between take-off and that point we had climbed to about 20,000 feet and started down again. Having forked up the smoked salmon somewhere short of Dungeness I handed back my tray over the long, red fields of northern France, with the sleek shadow of the Comet sliding across them. It was a magnificent ride, but what can one say about it that has not been said before? We were not really in any condition to appreciate it properly, but it was certainly smooth, fast and quiet. Cruising speed was about Mach ·85 and equivalent airspeed around 580 m.p.h.

Poor old Peter Pinfield was on his feet once more. As elected captain of a highly democratic team Peter had done a vast amount of detailed organising and reorganising, only to have everybody else continually suggesting a better way of doing everything. Throughout it all he had maintained an even temper, producing the polite reply on occasions when I should have been looking round for a blunt instrument. Now he wanted to tell us to fasten our belts and watch out for the deceleration when the engines went into reversed thrust. This they did in a big way, and before the aircraft had stopped we were sorting ourselves out in the aisle. We were going out in reverse order so as to claim an average time for the whole team, although each of us had paid a separate entrance fee so that if anyone dropped dead that would not invalidate the others' entries. Passports had been collected by the stewardess, and if there was a Customs inspection I did not see it.

This was rather a touchy moment, because we had been unable to rehearse the flight and the run into the Arc de Triomphe. If there was a crew bus and a car at the bottom of the steps we were to pile into them in a prearranged order and tear off to the gate where five taxis would be waiting. On the other hand, if the airport police had been co-operative and the Comet pilot clever with his landing, the five taxis would be somewhere on the airport very close to the nose of the Comet. As every individual had been detailed off to a particular seat in a particular vehicle, we had to bear two quite different procedures in mind, and adopt whichever was appropriate without any loss of time. In cold blood these details seem not very important, but when you are trying to clip seconds off a schedule for a 200-mile journey by thirteen people, they matter. It would have been desolating to see half the team tearing off in the wrong direction.

Several pairs of eager eyes were searching through the port windows. What was it—crew car or taxis?

" The taxis are there. Only about fifty yards away."

Good show! Down the steps, firmly held by volunteers and into the hands of two more volunteers who grabbed my arms, so that I should not fall, spun me round, and started me off in the right direction. It made me feel rather decrepit, but it was a good idea and presumably everyone got the same treatment. I did not stop to see.

The five taxis were waiting just on the other side of a ' crush-barrier ', lined up facing the road. All Citroën DS19's by the look of them. Good show again. Fourth taxi, left-hand rear door was my position, and before I was in, the first, second and third were away. Bill Simpson and Edwin Whitfield were there too, scrambling through their doors. We slammed them shut and were off, struggling to remember words of exhortation in French. In the excitement, all I could think of was *très bien,* which seemed rather feeble, and *shabash,* which was Hindustani and therefore not very suitable. Whitfield seemed to have the answer with " *Ventre à terre !* "

I do not suppose I shall ever know exactly what route we followed to the Etoile. We started at the south-west end of Runway 21 and the first thing that struck me as we tore out of the gate was how empty the roads were. I soon realised that this was the ' back road' from Le Bourget, the one you take to get out of the traffic on N.2, which is the main Lille and Soissons route passing the front of the airport. Very shortly, with much screaming of tyres, we joined Route Nationale Number One, the Amiens-Beauvais road, and headed for the Porte de la Chapelle.

Here again there had been two schools, those who thought the roads would be clear because the population of Paris would be eating Sunday lunch and then sleeping, and those who thought they would be crowding the streets. The first school must have been right—there was hardly a soul about and not a sign of the police. Perhaps the police felt they would rather not know about the rules we might be breaking. Along route N.1 things got slightly complicated. I had the utmost confidence in the car, which held the road wonderfully, and in the driver who clearly knew exactly what he was doing. The trouble was that no one else did.

Ahead of us and emerging out of side roads or going

round roundabouts were quite a lot of placid French papas out for a Sunday drive with no idea that five high-powered taxis travelling at almost 160 km.p.h. were about to descend on them. The question of road manners simply did not arise. Ruthlessness was the order of the day, and each time we bore down on a crowded round-about I shrank at the thought of all that innocent, shiny paintwork about to be gouged and scraped. Actually none of it was, but our public relations must have been terrible. Every corner and every crossing had its aftermath of furious or frightened drivers, according to temperament.

Despite his speed our driver was comparatively ortho-dox—at first. He had managed to dodge up into second or third place, but when the traffic got into a slight jam between a traffic island and a parked truck he drew up and stopped. Not so his colleague behind us, who swept up on the wrong side of the road and flew straight past the island and the traffic with a derisive toot.

I do not think we actually jumped any red lights, but several times we were across before the pink tinge had died off the glass. Always a good thing because it got us ahead of a block of traffic with a clear road until the next lot.

The cluster of big gasometers lying south of the Boulevard Ney marked the edge of the city proper, and my most dangerous moment came just there when Bill Simpson began wielding two scarlet umbrellas and nearly poked my eye out. They must have been under the seat, just another successful achievement in this most intricate organisation, and a sign of Bill's determination never to miss a publicity trick. Each umbrella had BEA-LINE SYNDICATE printed across it in large white letters. We restrained him from testing them inside the car and kept them for presentation to the ladies on arrival.

All along the Boulevard Ney, Boulevard Bessières and Boulevard Berthier (I think) we progressed exactly like one of those old Harold Lloyd comedies where the cops and the robbers go round every corner on two shrieking wheels and whizz through minute gaps in the traffic which close like traps behind them. Several times the driver rose to his feet and rode over a high spot like a steeplechaser. Twice we descended into the darkness of an underpass and popped out again like the devil in *Faust*. At the Boulevard Malsherbes there was a rather crafty left turn to bring us into the Avenue de Wagram. Our driver missed it, was redirected by a frantic hooting and pointing from one of his colleagues, swung straight across on oncoming traffic and pressed on regardless. A fascinating example of psychological warfare. Whitfield was the first to spot the Arc de Triomphe, sideways on at the far end of the Avenue de Wagram.

From there on we had it made. Or so we thought. Emerging into the Place de l'Etoile we saw our first and only policeman. He was nearly fast asleep on his feet, gracefully twirling his baton and doubtless dreaming about wine, women or song. Suddenly he saw our big race-badge and it galvanised him. His little moustache twitched with keenness, his right arm and baton shot out to hold up the other traffic and he nearly swallowed his whistle trying to blow it and wave us on at the same time. Round we went in a big sweep and then there was a calamity. The taxi slowed, the driver looked puzzled. None of the others were in sight and he clearly had no idea where the check-point was.

Impossible to run. We might take many minutes

finding the place. All three of us started gabbling instructions. That seemed to confuse him and he was already getting emotional with himself over his failure. There was also the small point that if he beat the schedule he was to get double the amount on the clock. As clearly and positively as I could I said, " Action Automobile—d'Iéna." Whether this did it or not I do not know, but we were already at the Avenue Marceau, the next one round the circle, and he obviously realised quite quickly that he could get down there, turn right and come out near the check-point just the same. Our anguish was considerable, but we can hardly have lost more than half a minute. Total time, Le Bourget to the Etoile, thirteen minutes.

One more scramble out of the car, two lines of crush-barriers, people shouting and pointing the way. We had no idea what they were saying, but the intention was clear and in another second or two we were all home and dry.

Our time was only just over the hour. Not bad for such a big team, average age about forty-five. Someone said we came from Le Bourget faster than Stirling Moss. We stood for photographs ; someone chalked up the official average time—one hour, two minutes ; scheduled airline time is three hours fifteen minutes. Then we retired to the bar, hot, dirty, sweaty, legs and hands shaking with effort, to drink pints of *citron pressé* or *coupe de champagne*, according to taste.

Next day the ' Daily Mail ' headline said, ' The champagne BEA-Line to Paris. Race-at-ease team arrives at the Arc in just over an hour.' They actually had the gall to say race-at-ease. It just shows you cannot believe all you read in the papers.

[' Maga ' February 1960

13

RE-BORNE WITH WINGS
John Brooks

On the threshold of the runway I stood, waiting. It reached out into the dark heart of a cumulus cloud growing up from the horizon as the sun rose higher. Down in the valley a bell spoke, and then another ; one by one they chimed in on the Sunday conversation. But to me the valley seemed infinitely remote. Watching the swelling tower of vapour it was as if the whole earth dipped and wheeled beneath me. With a shock of recognition I realised that I was experiencing again, was able to experience again, that poignant blend of eagerness and apprehension. But this was a quiet beginning to adventure.

Flying seems to generate in some people enough hot air to fill the balloon of the brothers Mongolfier. For a subject so essentially practical it seems to me to come in for more than its fair share of imaginative treatment : the loneliness of the welkin, all that cloud-side philosophy about the microcosm within the macrocosm and worse which, unchecked, leads on to an assumed empathy with the great universe itself. We whose daily task was to fly used to say, laughing, that if man had been meant to fly, he'd have been born with wings. Flying is the technique of controlling the movements of an aerofoil which is being propelled through the air at such a speed, and at such an angle of attack, that the lift resulting is sufficient to overcome the earth's attraction for the aircraft's mass. The chap who does this is known as the pilot. He does his best.

Of course flying can be a fever: one that lays low in the most exalted fashion. But the source of early inspiration soon degenerates into one only of perspiration. It is all in the game. What is, say, golf but co-ordination plus concentration? Neither golf nor flying is supposed to produce mystics or poets, though both have their most adhesive bores.

I am telling you this lest you should suppose that my head was in the clouds.

It was a long time since I had glanced up and first seen its peregrine shape silhouetted against the sky, darker than the cloud beneath which it circled and circled again. Out of curiosity I watched it. Have you ever noticed how, if you should read an unusual word, you will probably come across it again, perhaps three times in as many days? That was happening to me. The second time was when I was out on my Sunday walk—and it has to be something pretty vital to make me miss my Sunday walk. Then again when I was clipping a bush in the garden—trying a bit of topiary, of all things, to fill in the time. The postman pointed it out to me. How long, he wanted to know, could it stay up? I let him be in no doubt that I had not the very faintest idea. He was not put out. As his head bobbed by the hedge I caught his eye upon me, and it was full of a strange understanding.

Then there was that evening when I had been fairly brassed off after a day spent trying to fit an old garden shed up as a workshop. Frankly, I had no notion what I proposed to make in it if it had ever been finished, but it was Helen—you see, I had the idea she thought I would rather like it, so I pressed on with the thing rather than disappoint her. At last I heard the rattle of the tea things that I had been waiting for, and came indoors. Later I sat down to look the morning paper over once again. It happened to contain quite a lot of aviation news. I can remember all of it, so there's nothing the matter with my memory. There was an item about a new strike aircraft that was through its contractor's trials and was now starting its acceptance trials prior to going on squadron service. I had known it when it was a twinkle in its designer's eye (and when he was just plain Mister). Then there was an end-paragraph about one of our brainiest boys. I knew his background. A First in the Cambridge Engineering Tripos followed by the College of Aeronautics, Cranfield ; then into research at a time when the 'sound barrier' was all the thing. Now here he was delivering a paper to the Royal Aeronautical Society on stress problems associated with high skin temperatures on aircraft cruising at two-and-a-half times the speed of sound—the 'heat barrier'. Then a little story in which a journalist had done his best to be funny, but it was funnier for me, knowing the hero well. I first met him when I dropped in at Farnborough for something or other. He had just finished the Empire Test Pilots' School course. Very promising lad, they said, and how right they were. Now, it seemed, he had been forced to eject from an experimental aircraft, a single seater, just after take-off (and I would have bet anyone it was the old story of a runaway tail trim) and had come down unhurt beside a country road, where a rather startled old lady on a bicycle had told him he ought to be ashamed of himself. I could imagine the whole incident, but best of all I could imagine him telling the story afterwards.

I found I was standing up again, so I strolled out into the evening light, still chuckling. It was there. It circled three times in a silence so complete that I could hear a dog bark, a snatch of talk and a door slam. Then it rode away towards the sunset and the distant hill. I watched it out of sight.

One afternoon I got roped into a bowling match with a number of men, most of them much older than myself. One of the younger ones was landlord of the village pub. I had just sent up a fairish wood, wobbling it in close to the jack. I half-crouched, balancing the second bowl in my hand.

" Come on, then," the landlord rallied me, amused. " I should have thought you'd have had enough of them things by now!" Momentarily embarrassed, I knew that he had been following my gaze. It was eyes down to the green again. You do not have to be in a village long for them to know all about you.

I spoke to him casually in the pub that evening (" Why don't you go out for an hour or so?" Helen would say. " You're so restless.") Some youngsters, were they, I wondered. But he didn't know much about them except that they used the old war-time airfield on top of the hill, which was no better than a disgrace what with buildings all tumbling down and good land going to waste. . . . But a man who had cycled in from a neighbouring village knew the name of the ' secretarial ' who lived over by Bruntisford Common where the civil aerodrome serving the nearest manufacturing town was situated.

I looked up the name in the directory because it occurred to me that, if they were a keen bunch, they might welcome a little chat sometime on a flying subject. I knew nothing about gliding (frustrated power-pilots, a friend of mine in the early days used to call its few enthusiasts) but an aeroplane was always an aeroplane and I could surely bring something of interest. But in my note I simply asked if I might come and see them sometime, adding an unusually legible signature and leaving it at that. All I got back was a postcard.

I wonder if you have ever known the feeling that great orators must enjoy when with but a sentence they can silence a noisy rabble? I have. I merely remarked to the family, in the most casual way imaginable, that on the Sunday following I might possibly look in on the gliding people, just out of interest and if I had nothing more urgent to do. Then was silence. In a moment the usual exchanges started up again, but I knew that something irreversible had happened. Every glance in my direction had the quality of a ricochet, and references to the man of the house, in the third person, seemed to contain an embedded parable. My heirs discovered a vein of facetiousness, very poor quality stuff about flourishing almond-trees and burdensome grasshoppers. But Helen —about Helen I could not be sure. If I were fanciful I would say she had the air of one who, after much waiting, has heard the second shoe fall on the floor above. But you can never be sure through what queer lenses women view a man's world. And me, I'm just a practical chap. I was glad when Sunday came.

I came upon the airfield suddenly, where the winding hill ran out from among the trees ; an emasculated wind-sock tottering in a hawthorn hedge, a red brick control tower without an unbroken pane of glass, and something within that keened in the wind. The cups of a wind-gauge revolving above only emphasised its lifelessness. But nearby was a small hangar, freshly, bravely, painted. Beside it was a mast with two red balls at the head and two white crosses laid at its foot. In the language of airfield ground signals that meant Gliding in Progress. Impatiently I glanced at my watch.

I strolled out into the country silence that is in reality the sum of numberless complementary sounds. Then I had known the quickening and apprehension.

I tidied such fancies decently away and returned to the hangar. At least I would see them, through the window.

There were three. A chunky, indestructible-looking trainer and two sailplanes, one partly stripped in the middle of some overhaul. The sailplanes were even lovelier close-to than against the diminishing sky, with an insect's subtle aerodynamics—slender bodies giving them a poised look, cockpit canopies iridescing like compound eyes. But in their wings perfection was reached; slender arms, slightly elbowed, to take and embrace the air ; or rather, to put it properly, they were of a high aspect ratio, a design of maximum span to minimum chord, giving high lift at low speeds.

The gliders leaned together in beauty among a grotesque clutter of drums of cable, battered tool-boxes, crumpled maps, some dissolute hairy jackets and china mugs. A pair of huge yellow signalling bats lent the motley touch.

Yet the sight of it all rather dismayed me. Was I committing the hoary folly of revisitation? The dangerous search for time lost? And suppose, too ; suppose the familiar control pressures should prove no longer grateful

to my touch! There was my car and in my car was my
walking-stick and it was a Sunday morning. But oh, the
new silence when I returned!

Then they came in a great invasion of sound. There
was a van, a sports car, two irreproachable family saloons,
a Land-Rover off a farm and a tiny stuttering moped.
Like pirates they fell upon the hangar, all wearing
piratical knitted caps of vivid hues. Time, I reflected, did
not mean nothing to these gliding types; it just meant
something different. The gliders were summarily dis-
possessed and stripped naked. Sections were unzipped,
panels pulled off, heads burrowed into fuselages and legs
sprawled from beneath. No one was noticeably in charge,
yet everyone seemed to know what to do. The country
calm was chased out like a dog from a churchyard. For
myself, I began to feel like the Invisible Man.

After a while spent in addressing myself to the least
receptive parts of the human body, a pair of pliers
pointed out the secretary. Or rather the secretary's lower
half, the upper being jack-knifed into a sailplane cockpit.
I hrrmmed a bit. The secretary straightened, delightfully
flushed by inversion, tucking a rebel curl back into the
most gorgeous cap of all.

" Hullo, old boy," she said.

My number was made and her greeting in some way
seemed to dispose of my age.

" Good of you to get in touch. I'm called Drusilla."
(She wasn't, but it was something equally charming.)

After polite preamble she told me she had to fix a sailplane instrument before the Auster came over from
Bruntisford to give some aero-tows. Then when she was
half-way back into the sailplane again: " You don't come
from Bruntisford? Work there or something? No, of

course not. I just thought I'd come across your name somewhere. It gets us all like that after a bit."

" If you could just tell me who is the chief instructor."

" I am!" She laughed at the eagerness I must have been showing. " Don't worry. I'll fix you up a quick ride in this one after lunch. We always start 'em off with a sailplane ride just to whip up enthusiasm. Then it's down to the hard grind. But I'm sure Eddy would love a hand with the wires. Turbulent Eddy we call him. He's a hoot. See you, old boy." The final vowels sounded amphoric from the cockpit's depths.

Eddy, for all his vermilion hat slashed with turquoise, was a gratifyingly older hoot than I was. He was nimble and worked with an expert certainty that knew not condescension. I helped him lay out four hundred yard lengths of what turned out to be piano wire, ready for the car-towed trainer, inspecting every inch of it for kinks, and splicing where necessary. That is to say, Eddy did the splicing while I watched. I suspected he was the sort of man who could tie his shoe-lace with one hand.

" Soon get the hang of it," I assured him. " Fact is, I'm not long retired from the flying game myself."

Eddy nodded understandingly. " I was in boats at one time."

" Boats! Then it looks as if they picked the right man for the cable work——"

" *Flying-boats*." He looked up, listening. " Our Dru will soon be away."

The Auster appeared. It circled the airfield, a wing dipped enquiringly, then it dropped on to the runway beside us. We helped hitch the sailplane to it with sixty yards of fine nylon rope. Dru was going up to test the sailplane's instruments.

Work ceased. The batsman took his place at the sail-plane's wing-tip, bats held low before him. The Auster ambled forward, taking up the slack. The bats flashed up, waved violently above the head. The Auster's engine took on a note of urgent authority. It strained, momentarily snared, then gathered pace. Those holding the sailplane's wing-tips level started to run, arms outstretched as if reluctant to let it go. Delicately, disdainfully, it plucked itself off the ground, flying level a few feet up. Then the Auster itself became airborne and they crossed the distant boundary like climbers roped together, seeking the clouds where the lifting thermals breathed.

"You'll find it a bit funny at first," Eddy assured me as we returned to our chores. "But it can look funnier still."

Work on the nursery slopes got into full swing. We supervised the hoisting of the sailplane behind the tow-car and joined in holding our breaths for their eccentric returns. In the middle of it all the Auster came back alone and dropped its tow-rope to us before landing. Then Eddy left me to have a trip himself. "Keep my hand in," he explained. The car took him to the full height of the wire, with just time to stop at the end of the runway before Eddy released the tow. He made a meticulously accurate circuit of the field before coming in for a final approach that landed him right in front of the handling party. He started straight in on the chores again, but feeling, perhaps, that some reference was demanded: "Got to get it just right, see?" as if his flight had been in the nature of a demonstration, especially for me. "No engine to get you out of trouble. That's when accuracy counts. That's when you know whether you can fly."

That had a certain dustiness about it.

Dru had returned, coming swiftly upon us from up-wind, low enough for us to hear the sigh of the wind over her wings. Right overhead she pulled up into a long and lazy loop as if all heaven and all time were hers to do it in. Then from it she banked sharply, slipping off height a little, the lift-spoilers sprouting along her wings as she dropped in.

Lunch was an indeterminate affair that started some time or other and never really finished. Thermos flasks appeared, mysterious packets were disclosed. They munched holding wing-tips, they munched while the slack was taken up. I pondered the Sunday joint. They were of all ages. Though a few had flying pasts it was of the gliding present that they always spoke. I could contribute little among all the talk of Silver C's (cross-country flight of not less than thirty-two miles, climbing a thousand metres, five hours' duration) and the mysteries of finding ' lift '.

" The hats," I managed to ask, " what about the hats? " like some old leather-headed aviator who would be likely to use the word volplane for glide.

" Thermal hats," they assured me. " You'll never get very far without a thermal hat." Which, for me, meant that the most practical things have a mythology into which it is best not to pry.

" Now, old boy——"

People build gliders with an eye to lightness. What is not necessary is not there. But this cockpit (surely not a ' pilot's ' compartment) and this joystick (never conceivably a ' control column '), the half-dozen simplified basic flying instruments, even the elementary harness, were somehow not reassuring after being so long at the centre of a dialled and switch-studded electronic cage whose electronic complex was dedicated to the proposition that what goes up must come down—in one piece. I felt strangely vulnerable as willing hands pressed the canopy over us. And I made another discovery—that those butterflies, so long at rest, were still capable of an excited fluttering within me. Dru raised a manicured thumb and the batsman's arms came up. This was the moment ineluctable ; the point of no return, as when your first instructor opens the throttle for the first time on your first flight.

We trundled. We bumped, then suddenly the Auster was below us. We seemed hardly to be moving. A quick glance at the airspeed showed 35. Then the Auster seemed about to plough straight through the boundary hedge until I realised that its take-off had been hard to see from this angle. The fields unrolled beneath us like a slow-motion film, and I watched them to take my mind off this inching upwards. A glance at Dru ; she smiled back dreamily. The joystick before me roamed vaguely in sympathy with the one she held. The only sound was the lulling hiss of the airstream. Now we crept up under the shadows of the fair-weather puff-balls that had blown in the sky as the day wore on.

" Shall we find much lift?" I asked. She shook her head emphatically. " These are nothing," she dismissed the puff-balls. " There are some bumps over the corn stubble low down." I pointed to the towering cloud sentinels that had multiplied and now guarded the horizon. " You want it with jam on it," she laughed. " But they're too far away anyway."

Then the Auster levelled out. Its pilot waved. Dru tugged the red ball in the centre of the instrument panel and our nose nudged upward slightly as the tow-rope fell away. The Auster flung itself into a steep bank and fled out of sight beneath us. We hung ; I could almost have believed we had stopped. Then Dru turned to left and right, tightening the turns up (I was glad to find her showing off a little). I glanced slyly at the slip-and-skid indicator which showed us to be in perfect balance. Yet Dru was looking down at the sweep of countryside. I understood. This was what was called ' flying by the seat of the pants ', a sensitivity acquired out of sheer necessity by earlier fliers, and possessed by how many today, wedded, from the moment they lash themselves to their ejection seats, to the instruments before them?

She was smiling as if she could read my thoughts. My hands were folded in my lap like animals ready to spring. I must have looked away, embarrassed by her quizzical regard.

" You can come out now," she said. " I've remembered the name. I'm terribly sorry it took so long. Would you care to get the feel of her?"

If I was one of these fanciful chaps, this moment would have been heavily loaded with Significance: After Many a Season, the Return of the Native, whatever you will. Personally I won't. I never did have much sense of ooccasion.

" I have control," I said. And was immediately conscious that, with my feet on the rudder pedals and my right hand on the stick, my left, my throttle hand, was disconcertingly unemployed.

Frankly it was disappointing. The controls lacked the firm responsiveness of those I knew. There was a slackness, a sense of lost motion, after the tiny pressures of fast aircraft. After some trial and error, some very ham over-correction, during which I was painfully aware of my constant reference to the instruments, at last I seemed to have persuaded her into an optimum gliding angle— the best forward speed for the least descent. I relaxed. I steepened up a few turns but caught Dru's merry eye on the slip indicator and desisted. I trimmed her level again, feeling for the threshold of the stall. Dru showed no protest. At around 30 the sailplane shook herself fretfully, the stick shuddering in my hand. Then the nose dropped resignedly and in seconds she had picked up speed and unstalled herself again. A most friendly performance.

" Fun?" Dru asked.

" Spin?" I suggested.

She vetoed that at once. Not enough height, and as she said it she looked at me in a way which, had I not been in an exalted condition, I would have found highly significant. I was beginning to enjoy myself. For the truth which I had not yet admitted to myself was that I had been moving steadily towards one of those lovely, long, lazy loops. Casually I asked the speed for entry, and with only the barest perceptible hesitation she gave it to me. Professionally precise, I carried out the routine safety checks—airbrakes in, gyro instruments caged, harness tight. This was to be the moment of realisation.

Nose down, speed creeping up maddeningly slowly at first, then rising fast, the hiss of the wind becoming a croon. Check the dive and smoothly up with her—a quick glance along the wings to judge our accuracy at the vertical—the stick getting sloppy—suddenly no better than a clothes-prop in my hand, and a panic glance at an airspeed magically vanished. A hard pull back to get over the top and there was the horizon again, upside-down but wonderfully reassuring. Letting her fall into

the swooping dive in which the spirits soar with the world
a patchwork of fields and clustered farms on the end of
the nose. Then the gentle easing into level flight, the
letting out of breath and the forgetting; the forgetting
of those seconds of anxiety in the spacious satisfaction of
it all. Next time it would be perfect, because next time
I would remember that the airspeed must fall away more
quickly where there is no engine to give a leg-up.

For some moments I might have been alone in the sailplane. I glanced at Dru with justifiable confidence.

" I've got her," was all she said. I could not blame
her. My enthusiasm had carried me far, far downwind
of the airfield, which was a distant smudge on the ridge
only two thousand feet below.

Now she forgot me.

She flew with utter absorption, always a thought ahead,
hesitating beneath the puffs of cloud, getting the last
dram of lift before passing on to the next and from there
to a ride along the hill's crest, avoiding some woods but
making unerringly for a stubble, following the line of a
tarmac lane and getting a parting bump of air from the
metal roof of a Dutch barn as it gave up its store of the
day's warmth.

" You have her, old boy."

She gave the sailplane back to me poised like a hawk
over the boundary. A touch on the lift-spoilers, sinking
into the gradient of the wind, a long float across the grass
when it seemed she would never touch down, and then
the rumble of the single landing-wheel and the rasp of
the braking-skid. As if with a shrug, the sailplane settled
on one wing. In moments those same hands were helping
us off with the canopy.

The pace had slowed as the day drew in. The trainer was on its last flight. Tools were searched for. Eddy was winding in the cables. I drank luke-warm tea with Dru in the hangar.

"Of course it helps a lot," she assured me. "Helps?" I queried, bitter for how little help I'd been.

"To have ordinary straightforward flying behind you, yes. Saves a lot of the early donkey work. But then again, you people usually have such dreadful habits, have had them for so long that they're awfully hard to cure. It's just a matter of working at it."

This was one flight I put well and truly behind me.

"So when do I have my first lesson?" I asked.

She laughed. "You've had that, I think, haven't you? Now we'll get down to the really practical business of flying. I reckon you're going to be splendidly easy to teach, old boy."

And with that much comfort I washed up the mugs at the tap behind the control tower.

The departure was as reluctant as the arrival had been precipitate. With each glider nested home they seemed loath to leave, and there was much twilight talk of deeds yet to be done. When I drove down the lane again the wind-sock was black against the sky.

Supper was being laid as I came in. Helen had shoo'd the children out of the way. She was silent while I made the appropriate sounds of anticipation.

"You've enjoyed yourself," she said at last. It was a statement.

"By the way, about lunch——"

"We didn't expect you. You liked them? The gliding people?"

I had been early schooled to tell women what they want to hear rather than insult their imaginations by pedantic accuracy.

"Just a good bunch of chaps together," I said.

Thoughtfully she finished laying the table.

"We looked out for you to come over the house," she said. "Did you like the whatever-you-call-it—the flying part of it?"

It was in my mind's eye again; it might easily have been our own village, our own house, there before the nose as if you could reach out and touch it, easing from the dive.

"A piece of cake," I said.

"When you button it up!" In her most practical voice from the door: "I'll see you take some food next time."

I hesitated. "You don't mind or anything?"

"The relief of it! I thought you were never going to make up your mind. You like to make such a romance of the thing. You always have done and always will— let's hope so, John."

How can you explain to some people?

['Maga' May 1964

14

THE LONG WAY BACK
D. E. Charlwood

We had spent eleven months of the past fifteen in places as far apart as Madang and Limerick, always with the same task: the selection of men for air traffic control in Australia.

Interview had succeeded interview, each associated in our memories with clammy handshakes and intent faces. And everywhere we went each of us had heard the other ask questions on the same subjects until we could have acted the other's part from memory with every mannerism complete.

In 1963 the search had taken us to Britain for almost four months; this year we had stayed longer; indeed our memories of the two visits tended to merge and we began to wonder at times where our homes lay.

On 12th August the 1964 task ended. That night, from the gallery of the 'Adelphi', I watched Marcel Marceau take a final bow. The applause ended and the audience moved out into warm darkness.

It was almost eleven o'clock but traffic still flowed steadily down the Strand. I turned on to Waterloo Bridge and stood looking downstream to the floodlit dome of St

Paul's. Here was fit place to take one's leave. Tomorrow morning, Amsterdam, next day Edmonton, then the long crossing of the Pacific ; but tonight a brief farewell to the dome floating above its city, beneficent and in some way representative of the people of the surrounding land.

I walked slowly back along the Strand and round Australia House corner. By St Clement's clock it was eleven thirty. I should have gone to bed early. No doubt Eric Jewell was by now asleep ; he was much more prudent than I. But then we might never come back and one must bid London farewell with due affection.

" They are reminiscent of W.A.A.F.s' voices," I said.
" W.A.A.F.s' voices?"
" On Control R/T. Remember?"
" Passengers for Venice," said the cool voice. " Flight BE134 to Venice is departing now. Please have your boarding passes ready. . . ."
They typify their country, I thought. It is the same on railway stations ; the voices are precise but kindly. By inflexion they say, " Please listen all harassed mothers, all weary businessmen, while I speak to you." In the New World it was different; information of this sort tended to be rapped like an order.

The call came for Amsterdam passengers. Eric folded his newspaper and tapped out his pipe. This, I thought, is reminiscent of a filial farewell Perhaps no one who was here in the war years would feel otherwise. We might wish that our mother would tidy her hair a little, but of her maternal compassion for her sons, indeed for all men, we have no doubt. She watched us depart with her rain clouds drawn about her ancient shoulders.

221

In my memory Amsterdam was a place to avoid. In those other years it would lie hidden in darkness until someone blundered over it. Then flak and searchlights would begin. When the action was ended all visible activity would cease and darkness would return, but one was left conscious of helmeted malevolence in the underlying shadows.

Today there was only grey cloud and occasional passing planes hurtling at closing speeds of eight or nine hundred miles an hour. We had come this way to join the Amsterdam-Edmonton flight of the following day. Alberta was my wife's native province ; by returning this way I could spend a weekend among friends and relatives.

Below us a magician's cloth was removed and, spread to the horizon, were sodden fields squared by canals and rows of flats, their roofs wet in drizzle ; and cars and cows and bicycles. Then, approaching low over them, we landed.

After walking all the afternoon beside the canals we slept heavily, but at a quarter to six next morning I heard movements about the room. It was Eric's habit to rise early, my own to rise late.

" Jewell," I said bitterly, " hasn't it struck you that today is going to be elongated enough without your adding to the beginning of it?"

" I'm going for a walk," he answered impenitently.

From my bed I could see through the narrow gap between our building and the next. Early light fell on the greenish water of the Herensgracht and on to tall houses beyond. Amsterdam was much as I remembered it from a stay in this same little hotel seven years before ; the golden wood of doors, the aroma of cigars, the benign chiming of bells all about the city, the silver, the pewter, the Delft, the rich foodstuffs, the verticality of the place with its narrow building fronts and steep stairs.

At breakfast time there was a mixture of nationalities seated in the small dining-room. Perhaps with malice aforethought our host sat us with an Australian tourist and an Englishman. The volume of the Australian's voice embarrassed us. He had been travelling for three months he said, with a desperate look in his eye.

" Too long. One cathedral after another—you see one, you see the lot."

We made non-committal sounds and began eating rapidly.

" They told me I should go to Wales, where my family came from. Said it was wild. Wild! I'll tell you what: its wilder in my backyard than in Wales."

We studied our boiled eggs closely.

" It's the hygiene that gets me more than anything. Not so bad here, but England—! Fish lying on marble slabs right out in the streets—"

" We do have a good deal to learn in this regard," the Englishman murmured seriously.

" And then there's the dogs. Any time you're likely to have a dog right at a café table. I reckon the dogs over there get better treatment than a lot of the people."

He was blundering on to holy ground. We bolted the last of our breakfast and left.

During his dawn wanderings Eric had come upon the house of Anne Frank. He led me to it and we stood at the edge of the canal waiting for the plain-looking warehouse to open. A small group of people were at the door ; most of them visitors from Israel.

When it came time to go in, we climbed the stairs

with the strange sensation that we were entering, not a building, but the mind of the girl who had written of it. As the bookcase swung back it was difficult to believe that this was the way the jackbooted men had burst in twenty years earlier to end the hopes of the pitiful group sheltering there.

Of course, such things could never happen again. The men concerned had no doubt been found ; the country which had perpetrated these acts had been so dealt with that it could never repeat them. The modern, tolerant city outside the door was there to reassure us.

" These are pictures Anne and Margot cut from magazines and pasted here."

We looked at the posed stage and film stars of the early war years and at a photograph of a Michelangelo head and another photograph of a house among poplars by a canal.

" And here are the girls' heights, probably marked by Mr Frank."

We were intruding—and yet, perhaps she had not been wholly unaware that her life was to have significance.

Here were Mr Frank's maps showing the Allied progress after D-Day. The little group had almost won out ; almost.

" These steps go to the attic," said the flat voice of the girl leading us. " You will remember that Anne refers in her diary many times to them."

" It is the—contrast," whispered a woman in English. " The young girl and the—the—"

A smartly-dressed girl of sixteen or seventeen, her hand-luggage labelled VANCOUVER, is explaining to her father while they wait for their departure that "two threepences equal one shilling". He, in unprevailing, paternal fashion rather thinks two sixpences equal one shilling. She laughs indulgently. Fathers are so quaint. Terribly, terribly slow to see things, but sometimes quite cute.

"Do you think Harry will meet us with the ranch wagon?"

"I sure hope so. What with all this junk you and your mother have bought—"

"Passengers for Edmonton, Calgary and Vancouver who need assistance or are travelling with small babies are kindly requested to preboard via gate number seven."

An elderly couple, frail-looking, walk slowly on to the tarmac hand in hand. Somewhere a baby is crying.

"I guess this will be the longest lunch-time of our life," says father to daughter. "Lunch-time here when we leave and lunch-time when we get to—ah, 'bout Edmonton, I'd say. How long's that?"

"Eight and a half hours. My poor fig-gure!"

Our call came and we stepped off Europe into a whale-shape with rows of disproportionately small windows; a monster which on the tarmac looked stranded and helpless.

Once its jets had started the creature's dignity began to return and it uttered boasts of what it would achieve when it broke free. In contrast to its bellicose roaring came a deliberate Canadian voice over the cabin address system: "Our flight time to Edmonton is estimated to be eight hours forty minutes and we shall be flying at altitudes between thirty-five and thirty-nine thousand feet. Route distance from Amsterdam to Edmonton is four thousand four hundred and ten miles. Lunch and dinner will be served during the flight."

The monster began screaming its intentions. It hesitated in a holding bay, cursing an incoming aircraft and beating its inflated chest impatiently. The Canadian let it on to the runway and gave it its head. Immediately it raced away, flinging hangars and masts and parked aeroplanes behind it in fury, faster and faster ; the control tower, an enormous advertising sign, runway lights by the score, then the entire spinning globe. . . . Already they were in miniature, and of trifling importance. A few white clouds were flung after them. I tried to see Amsterdam, but it was whirling behind us, the sun glinting briefly on canals and glasshouses. A glimpse of bare-looking tulip fields, then of innumerable currant-sized creatures on a beach, then cloud.

We crossed the English coast near Hull, but before I could recognise so much as the familiar junction of the Trent and the Humber the whole scene had been relegated to the east and the voice interposed again, asking us to look at the map provided.

" We will be following the red line as shown on the map, until we reach Prestwick in Scotland. From there we will cross the North Atlantic just south of Reykjavik in Iceland. We will cross the east coast of Greenland where the line intersects it." This was near a settlement marked ' Ikateq '. " On the west coast of Greenland we will pass almost directly over Sondrestrom. From Sondrestrom we will follow the centre one of the three red lines on the map." This line passed over a nameless part of Baffin Island north of Cape Dyer, then on across Foxe Basin and the north-west corner of Hudson Bay and so over a wilderness of lakes. " This line we follow right to Fort Mount Murray and on into Edmonton. The weather forecast indicates that the westerly winds will not be strong and that we should make fairly good time. Our speed over the surface is five hundred and sixty-five miles per hour."

Before the immensity of the journey could begin to deter us, menus were summoned up and our minds were diverted to ' puff pastry with salpicon of sweetbreads '. This was a mere beginning. It looked as if coffee would be served inside the Arctic Circle.

We had begun our second course, sunk in an indolent superiority engendered by cabin service and altitude, when the western edge of Britain appeared from under cloud. We were over Prestwick, but the Great Glen was a stone's throw to the north, a deep blue crevice in tumbled hills.

> *From the lone shieling of the misty island,*
> *Mountains divide us, and the waste of seas ——*

Not mountains ; thirty-two thousand feet of translucent air, yet we were no less remote than they had been. To Lochaber we were invisible, invisible even to Glasgow— unless the sun touched our fuselage at such an angle that we flashed briefly, on some upturned eye. The Scotland down there might have been at the dawn of history. It carried no conviction to say that there was Jura and that that other island was Mull ; remarkable maps of Jura and Mull perhaps, but not the reality.

> *And we in dreams behold the Hebrides ;*

A dream ; no more than a dream.

The Atlantic was invisible ; even the cloud that covered it was twenty thousand feet down. At these altitudes the monster was at home, flexing its wings, jet-mouths roaring like far surf. We, sitting inside in business suits were so many anachronisms it was obliged to tolerate.

"Eyeshade for you, sir—it will be a long day."

We undid the small packages and found black, eyeless masks. Before donning his, Eric cast a last offended glance at his watch, as if it had been deliberately deceiving him.

Somewhere my mind became befuddled by enigmas of time. If we were to remain here in latitude sixty-seven or sixty-eight with adequate supplies of fuel, would it not be simple enough to race along in daylight indefinitely? And when aircraft became faster would the sun not appear to set in the east? Or rise in the west, for that matter?

I lifted my eyeshield to glance from the window and was startled to see curdled miles of pack-ice and, ahead, mountains rising out of snowfields.

As this discovery of Greenland became general, visors were raised and passengers began visiting each others' windows. Far down, glaciers crept to a grey, ice-laden sea.

"Today you can see it well," said the man opposite. I was struck by the gentleness of his voice. He and his wife were the elderly pair we had seen go aboard hand in hand.

"You have seen it before?"

"We have flown the Atlantic each year for the past sixteen years. Each time we think it is the last, because we are now both over eighty."

Sitting alone behind them was an English schoolboy of fourteen or fifteen. "We're coming to a river," he said.

It was broad and grey with white cakes of ice floating in it and the tongue of a glacier reaching down to the water, the tongue white and cracked. Soon after this a clear line of demarcation appeared where the snow ceased and a grey country of fiords and valley lakes began, treeless, grassless and empty.

The boy was no longer held by the scene. He lit a cigarette which smoked itself between his childlike lips.

It was then six-fifteen p.m. London time ; ten-fifteen a.m. Edmonton time. We should have been seating ourselves in The Black Sheep in Woburn Walk for our evening meal.

" Have you slept?"

" Not really."

The first officer looked into the cabin, a lynx-eyed, youthful-looking man—finished training at the end of the war, we decided. Yes, Greenland was a harsh country, though some of the Danes enjoyed their posting there, he had been told. He passed on down the cabin. I could accept the flight crew as voices, but it was faintly surprising to see again that they were mortals.

Greenland had gone. Three ships were clustered in the lonely, slate-coloured sea, then they, like Greenland, Iceland and the Hebrides were cast into the east as desperate offerings to Night.

The Canadian voice spoke. We were approaching Foxe Basin at the top of Hudson Bay.

In these freezing latitudes, did Hudson and his son still gaze unseeing on to walls of ice, or had three hundred and fifty summers removed all trace of them? White stratoform cloud was drawn decently over the remote sea. I retired to the privacy of my eyeshade.

The steward appeared. " A drink before dinner, sir?"

" But we have not long eaten."

" Ah, that was four hours ago."

" It's nine p.m. stomach time," said Eric, studying his watch. But we were doomed to defeat, were humiliated in fact by boneless Cornish chicken. We were unable to do justice even to champagne.

The indecency of it all struck me. Somewhere, seven miles below us, my father-in-law, when a relatively young man of sixty, had paddled a canoe the length of Lake Athabasca with Edsel, his nephew. They had paddled to Fond du Lac and had then portaged in country where the black flies had almost deprived them of their sanity. They had been looking for gold, but had found nothing. I doubted that they had carried boneless Cornish chicken.

Tonight or, rather, this afternoon, I would meet this same Edsel. Last time I saw him, he had led me all day along a stream in the Rockies. We had both been armed with fishing rods. His he wielded with diabolical cunning, catching trout whenever the fancy took him, whereas my line was as much in the trees as the stream. He had been, and no doubt still was, a man of immense strength, capable of carrying two hundred pounds of venison for miles overland.

While we were still within sight of Lake Athabasca the covering of stratus broke, revealing a country dark green and entwined by rivers, without sign of habitation. Into Lake Athabasca flowed the Athabasca river and on the river, more than two hundred miles south of the lake, was Fort Mount Murray. We passed over it at ten past two, Edmonton time.

I looked on to the compact group of buildings beside the vigorous river. The place had a fort-like appearance still and an air of isolation. The river's swirls and rapids were clear in the sun, but as silent as a picture ; indeed, what was this mode of travel but a series of pictures? No sound, no cold, no scent.

"We will be starting our descent in eleven minutes and will be landing at Edmonton in thirty-five minutes."

Edmonton had meant much to me. I could remember first coming to it one night in 1941 and seeing from the train the Avro Ansons of the Air Observers' School standing in brilliantly-lighted hangars. I had never flown before and was about to begin. Within a few weeks our men were to know the surrounding countryside well. We had been flown by bush pilots to whom our struggling flights must have seemed tame stuff indeed. Oakes, Irwin, Johannsen—what giants they had seemed to us!

I suppose by the time we left the Air Observers' School most of us associated various places in Alberta with our own personal triumphs and disasters—the failure of some lake or town to turn up on E.T.A., a successful interception, the painful effort of kneeling at an open window to sketch at low level a railway bridge over the Saskatchewan river. And I remembered seeing one night a small scattering of lights, marking the village of Vermilion. I had no notion then that Vermilion would have significance for me the rest of my life.

And a day I still remembered with a sudden contraction of the heart: the day word reached us that only two of the Edmonton course a year ahead of us had survived a Bomber Command tour of operations.

The monster had descended to the tops of cumulus clouds, but there was still little sign of civilisation other than a whitish road meandering through dark-green country between numerous lakes.

Farmlands with swathed wheat in golden, geometric patterns appeared quite suddenly. About them were

231

straight fences—so handy once for checking compasses because each ran north-south or east-west. Then frequent farmhouses appeared, each dominated by an enormous barn ; uncut crops then, and Aberdeen-Angus cattle and there, a smudge on the horizon, the city and its guardian Beaverhill Lake, placed there by a beneficent Providence to guide embyro navigators home.

Now we were close to earth : grain elevators, a farmer on a tractor, an oil pump, cars on a road. No longer tulip fields or canals or step and neck houses. These had been relegated to darkness on the other side of the earth. Two hundred feet, one hundred, touch. The roar of reverse thrust.

A magnificent new terminal building reared out of the prairies, isolated and gleaming, waiting patiently for the high-density traffic of the future. The voices greeting us were dwarfed by the shining immensity of lounges and halls. And we were not yet quite with them, these earth-bound people ; our shattered souls were strewn across four thousand miles of earth and sea.

The day was clear and still, the sun pleasantly warm, one of those delightful prairie days of late summer.

As we drove towards the city Edsel said, " We are having a few of the folk in for supper this evening...."

By the time it grew dark, daylight had lasted twenty-three hours. Bed then at two o'clock, twenty-eight hours after waking in Amsterdam.

" I'll make it up in the morning," I said.

" Well," Edsel replied apologetically, " the only day we could arrange to go out to Vermilion and Dewberry was tomorrow."

As our car set sail next morning a hundred and fifty miles eastward across the prairies it seemed perfectly natural, perplexingly natural, to be where I was. The long, straight road with its ditches to either side lay like a surveyor's rule through the wheat lands of Vegreville, Lavoy, Ranfurlie, Mannville—'Mannville, population 699', where my wife had begun her teaching career. It was rolling country with woods called locally 'bluffs' and, in many of the hollows, small 'sloughs'. Clusters of grain elevators dominated each town and could be seen miles off like the tabernacles of some new religion.

All that day I spent with prairie people. Three of the older ones had been early settlers in the district. There was Uncle Ed, eighty-one and white-haired, who had worked on the family mine in Western Australia. He had gone then to Marble Bar to work on the 'rabbit-proof' fence put up in a vain attempt to keep rabbits from the west.

"Well, sir, the sun was so hot you daren't put a crowbar on the ground."

From the fence he had gone to a log hut to pioneer these same prairies, to temperatures of sixty below zero.

About these early homesteaders there was something monolithic, something reminiscent of great statues in a valley doomed to flooding. They were still holding their ground with dignity as the water level rose. In time, the flood of custom-built, pre-packaged mediocrity would cover them ; but today they remained as monuments to another age.

Ten of us sat to midday dinner. Turkey and cranberry sauce, sweetcorn and butter, green peas. . . .

"Would you say grace, Uncle Ed?"

Last time I had heard this fervent growl was six years ago when my children had been awed, as if hearing the voice of an Old Testament prophet on close terms with

God.

"Amen," we said.

"Now, will you pass the dishes round? I do hope the vegetables are hot."

Outside the sun was bright. I could see into the garden through the double glass window my globe-trotting father-in-law had put in during one of his periodic visits. It was the only window that remained free of frost in winter. Probably his next job had been building a cupboard when he visited us in Melbourne.

By the time we left, it was nearly ten o'clock and had long been dark. The night miles erupted into brief garishnesses of little towns strung from east to west: youths and girls twitching round a jukebox; age sagging on a step; a motel importuning the stars; then darkness again till the next town. I began nodding and finally dozed, conscious still of the drumming wheels. The drumming would sometimes become confused in my mind with the surf-sound of the jets.

"Where are we?"

"Vegreville," said Edsel.

"I must have dozed."

I hung on to consciousness and let my memory continue the recollections. I had been dreaming of the barracks in Edmonton, the day the first snow fell. We had our usual route march, the Canadians swinging along easily, the Australians slipping and sprawling on the frozen surface.

"You can see the glow of Edmonton now."

We ate a 'brunch' of blueberries and cream at eleven next morning. I walked to a high point above the river. Once I had seen the Saskatchewan river from here,

234

thickening with early ice. Later we had walked on to it to watch men with long saws cutting blocks of the blue-ish stuff for summer use. Now the water was flowing vigorously, the sun glinting on its whorls.

Watching there, I became two men: one fully aware that this city was a brief stopping place from which I must go on, the other urging the need to relax into its rhythm of normal living. This second was tempted to slip into the round of Edmonton life. Today could be pleasantly spent on Sunday visiting, this evening there was a barbecue, then bed at a normal hour. And in the morning? In the morning—ah, there was the rub: Vancouver, San Francisco and the waiting Pacific.

And, of course, it was so. There, shining in the early sun, lonely between earth and sky, was the terminal building again. In a few moments it and the city itself had been flung into the discarded east.

Before there was time to prepare the mind for them, the great peaks of the Rockies were staring in at the windows, gaunt, snow-capped and disapproving, and between them the Fraser and the Columbia. I looked down at the glinting threads of the rivers, trying to associate them with those first explorers and their fearful canoe journeys, but it was all too remote ; much too remote.

In San Francisco the evening was cold and our news was depressing. It had availed us nothing to have hurtled from Vancouver at six hundred m.p.h., for our Sydney plane was four hours late ; we faced a wait of eight hours.

A cloth of fog stratus was flung from the Pacific across the coastal hill, its edge dragging over the city. As we drove from the airport the working populace poured homeward, caparisoned in gleaming automobiles. The streams thundered through packed wooden suburbia, which in a few years would be slums.

We walked determinedly up Nob Hill and through Chinatown while fog writhed about the tallest buildings. After dark the streets became bleak, and somewhere in the bay a foghorn sounded. We wandered doggedly for four hours, then gave up and turned back to the airport.

It was almost one a.m. when a telescopic ramp attached itself like an umbilical cord to the door of our aircraft. As we shuffled aboard we caught an intimate glimpse through the ramp windows of the crew sitting in the cockpit immersed, priest-like, in the holy business of pre-take-off check. Although we could not hear the words spoken, I had no doubt that placatory prayers were being offered, petitions too, that the monster would bear us safely through the parallels of night. The prospect of seventeen hours in its belly did not bear considering.

We were towed out backwards, then all the waves of the Pacific began thundering at our flanks. The monster quivered and moved out. In a holding bay it hesitated, flexed itself and, like a long jumper, rushed at top speed and leapt into the night.

The cabin lights were put out and fitful sleep came ; dim consciousness too that the priestly men were staring ahead through the monster's brow, were conversing with earthbound brethren to whom all this human cargo was a mere speck of light on a radar screen. . . .

My watch showed five-fifteen when we walked into the warm, scented night, barely awake. With difficulty I interpreted this as Edmonton's dawn of tomorrow, since I hadn't touched my watch since leaving there.

" Jewell, just what is the damned time?"

He muttered that it was two-fifteen.

A sign said: WELCOME TO HONOLULU. We trudged into a reception room and passed before an official for something called 'a walk through customs check' and before another whose function I failed to comprehend—perhaps it was to ensure that none of us fell asleep and was left to become a burden on the country's economy.

We trailed outside after a guiding hostess, past coconut palms nodding under fluorescent lights and were delivered into a large, terrazzo-floored waiting-room with one open wall. We leaned at this, staring seawards. Behind us, passengers from various parts of the world drowsed and smoked and stared. Music was being piped from somewhere, soft and inconsequential.

Our wavering attention was caught by a detachment of helmeted soldiery moving out of the night, advancing into the room in good order. A firing squad? A group of survivors from somewhere? They moved smartly into the coffee lounge.

"There's our call." Eric began moving immediately, as if walking quickly might bring him sooner to Sydney.

Two young passengers, clearly of Australian origin, went aboard ahead of us, the girl with flaxen hair, a lightly-tanned skin, a lei of frangipani round her neck; the man more deeply tanned, the turned-down brim of his hat wide, like the verandah around his homestead.

The rush of ingested air began. The blonde girl stared through the window to catch a last glimpse of her honeymoon world, but saw only a reflected girl staring back. Then it all rushed away from her, fell below and was left glittering beside the sea, then that too was gone and she hurtled towards forty years of domesticity.

"Something to drink, sir?"

" At three in the morning?"

" Well, it's midnight Suva time really. We are just coming into Wednesday."

So we were flinging away days now, as well as countries.

A disembodied Australian voice gave our E.T.A. Nadi at six a.m., Suva time. Six hours! Even to the Kon-Tiki men the Pacific could scarcely have seemed as large ; even to Cook. . . .

We submerge ourselves in the world of half-dreams again, occasionally opening our eyes to stare hopefully in the direction we imagine to be east. Eric lies twisted like an embyro chicken in an egg.

The hours trudge across our eyelids until a streak of red sky appears off the port quarter. Why that way? Is that east then? The sun god, having devoured our gifts of islands, cities, even a day, is about to overtake us. When next I open my eyes a sick square of sunlight is shining on the cabin wall, but to starboard there is semi-darkness.

A to-and-fro movement of stewards begins and orange juice is served. Eric stammers irritably that it reminds him of hospital: " Thermometers, early morning wash and all the rest of it. No use saying you only want to go to sleep."

The light grows a little. We can see flocks of purplish clouds under a cobalt sky, a scene somehow lonely and discomforting. While I am shaving up forward, staring into bloodshot eyes, the announcement is made that we have crossed the International Date Line. My Edmonton watch says midday Tuesday, the day that never was. The purplish clouds are changing to white and the sun is beginning to shine.

" That must be Fiji ahead." It is the tired voice of the embyro chicken. Uncoiled now, he is staring indifferently on to a land of dark colours—dark green of plantations and fields, dark blue of jagged mountains. We are descending like a bird out of the night, with night still clogging our senses.

About the waiting-room at Nadi there was a quiet atmosphere of early morning. Outside the air was hushed and still, heavy already with the coming heat. Smoke rose from cooking fires at huts beyond the edge of the airport, but few people were abroad. From the public address system ' Hawaiian ' music oozed—a strumming of guitars and subdued, nostalgic ululations of female voices.

We found a palm trunk to lean against and there we waited, eyes half closed. Out to sea ponderous galleons of cloud were bearing down on the island ; others were building up over the mountains.

" Looks like a rough trip out of here," said someone pacing the lawn near us. Rough, smooth, what did it matter? Sleep was all that mattered—sleep and an end to travelling.

The monster lurched and quivered as we turned inside the mountains and dodged through corridors of cloud out to sea. Our minds began reaching out to Sydney.

After a couple of hours I cupboarded myself between the chrome and mirrors of the toilet to change my clothes. The close intimacy of the place was broken startlingly by a voice saying beside me, " It may interest the technically-minded if I give a few details of our performance. Out of Nadi our all-up weight was one hundred and ten tons ; when we land at Sydney it will be eighty-five tons. The difference is the fuel we will use up at the rate of five tons an hour. We are developing twenty-three thousand six hundred horse-power and our air-speed is five hundred and seventy miles per hour."

At the end how could one explain this sort of speed? The fact that St Paul's dome and Anne Frank, and Greenland and Uncle Ed, could be compressed into—how long was it? These were places and people that all one's life had been widely separated, except perhaps in dreams.

I knotted my tie and went back to my seat. We were descending peacefully, the surf sound hushed, as if the monster were humming to itself . And then, hazy, ahead, lay a long indented coastline. It did exist then, our country. Soon, the entrance to Sydney Harbour, with waves breaking silently against the Heads and Captain Phillips' great city packed beside the blue water.

Eric smiled wanly. "Are you going into the office in the morning?" he asked innocently.

[' Maga ' February 1965

15

AQUILINE ACTIVITY

James Montgomery Robinson

I

I have a vivid childhood memory of two wedge-tailed eagles attacking a wallaby near a large stone outcrop on a sunny Australian hillside. One of the big birds had an iron grip high on the wallaby's neck, and was belabouring the unfortunate creature's head with its wings, while the second was tearing at the lower back with its curved beak.

It was a Sunday afternoon in the late Twenties, and an uncle, the proud possessor of a shiny new motor car, had taken my parents, my young brother and me for a drive in the bush. We halted at the edge of the quiet country road, some two hundred yards from this unquiet scene of carnage.

I desperately wanted to help the wallaby, but my father and my uncle bade us wait. Having no gun, they grabbed sticks and set off up the hillside. The eagle which had been tearing at the wallaby gave the alarm, and as the two men approached, both birds flew off, climbing steeply, to circle overhead and withdraw. The wallaby was too badly injured to run away and my uncle quickly put it out of its misery.

I also remember, vividly, the thumping I got from a bigger boy when I related the story at school. Out of a feeling of obligation to my audience, I may perhaps have substituted a large old-man kangaroo for the wallaby, but the account of the co-ordinated attack by the two eagles was pretty accurate. Nobody relishes being doubted when he has told some of the truth.

This bigger boy went on to assure me that a wedge-tail eagle would not have much difficulty in swooping down and carrying off a chap of my size, that two of them acting in concert would find it an absolute piece of cake, and that if I went around telling any more similar yarns, this fate would almost inevitably overtake me. While I did not actually believe this, I thought it prudent to take no unnecessary chances, and kept a wary eye out for eaglehawks (as we called the big eagles) for a few days, sticking closely to the whole truth for about the same period.

A few years later, my brother and I, guests for the Christmas holidays on another uncle's property, were able to carry out some research on eaglehawks. The *modus operandi* was simple. The fowl-house was situated inside a large run, which was wired along the sides and over the top to thwart the eaglehawks' interest in my aunt's poultry.

Shooing the poultry, including a few hens with small chickens, outside the fowl-house, we took post within— I with the muzzle of a single-barrelled shotgun (which I had only recently been permitted to use) just protruding through an aperture, and an extremely limited field of vision, my brother acting as a sort of Fighter Controller, from another peep-hole.

We seemed to wait for hours before we had a target—about the time it takes two lads to drink a bottle of lemonade. My brother described the eaglehawks' approach, so that I was ready to shoot, when, near the bottom of its dive, it was baulked by the overhead netting. I blasted away and it plumped in a heap on the wire.

It was a male weighing just over seven pounds, with a six-foot-three wing-span, and a length of three feet. The beak was dark brown with a whitish cere, the irises of the eyes were yellow, and the feathers, except for reddish streaks at the nape of the neck, black right down to the powerful, razor-sharp whitish talons, which gave the bird the appearance of wearing shaggy pants.

The eaglehawk is not protected in any Australian State, and at that time it was gazetted in some States as vermin, with a price on its head. Landowners were invariably delighted to see them killed, as was my uncle, who gave my brother and me half-a-crown each (plus a cartridge) in exchange for each head, on which he could claim a bounty. This seemed to us a profitable enterprise, and we too were pleased; but not so our aunt, because the firing of the shotgun in their midst meant that the fowls neglected to lay for some few days.

By venturing further afield with a ·22 rifle we succeeded in bagging a few more specimens. No concessions were made to sportsmanship. We did not in fact get any on the wing; it was difficult enough to hit sitting birds; for they perched majestically in the tops of dead gum-trees, and usually flew away before we could get lethally close. The heaviest kill was a female weighing just over eight pounds.

I found a number of disused nests—large untidy plat-forms—high up in the gum-trees. They were littered with the bones of rabbits, wallaby, and smaller birds, but nary a thing resembled the remains of a sheep. And there was another surprising thing about the nests. It was not unusual for them to include in their structure branches weighing up to ten pounds, far heavier than we believed any eaglehawk could take off with. Nor could the branches have fallen from higher up in the trees. We were puzzled about this, and had almost come to the conclusion that they must have been air-lifted into position by two eaglehawks working together, but eager as we were to find some startling solution we could not quite accept that.

One old-timer, renowned throughout the district as a teller of tall tales, assured us that the eaglehawk perches on the end of one of the lower dead branches of the tree in which the nest is to be built. By bouncing up and down, the eagle uses its weight to break the branch, which falls. During the fall, it is snatched in mid-air by the bird, whose air-speed is sufficient to enable it to climb up, with its burden, to a point slightly higher than the nest, and then drop the branch into the desired position.

The old chap said that eaglehawks will fly with small sticks, let them fall and then dive and catch them in mid-air just for fun; also that they will drop sticks into bushes where rabbits or hares may be hiding, so as to frighten them into the open where they may easily be caught.

Certainly I have often seen eaglehawks carrying rabbits. They appear to kill the animals by crushing them with their talons. Twice I have seen rabbits either squirm loose from an eagle's grip, or be deliberately dropped, from heights of well over a hundred feet. The end result for the rabbit was the same either way.

During a few days of heavy summer rain, when it was too wet to go out of doors, we set to and diligently bombarded the Gould League of Bird Lovers with carefully concocted, graphic ' eye-witness ' accounts of these amazingly intelligent feats of the eaglehawk. In due course we received cautiously typed acknowledgments, thanking us for this information.

In later years I read serious accounts of these alleged happenings, but I have never met anybody, apart from the old chap, who claimed actually to have witnessed them.

Our bluff was called on another occasion. We had read that the eaglehawk was larger than both the American eagle and the northern hemisphere Golden Eagle, but not so big as the monkey-eating eagle of the Philippines. We were quite satisfied with the first two contentions, but disinclined to accept the third. Moved by fervid nationalism, we wrote to the Naturalists' Column of a leading daily, claiming that we had killed an eaglehawk with a ten-foot wing-span. We were politely asked for a photograph of one or both of ourselves with this remarkable bird.

A girl cousin laboriously made a two-thirds scale tape-measure. My brother and I were dazzled by this potential for arithmetical chicanery, but with great reluctance we had to abandon the idea. It was true that an eaglehawk with a wing-span of a little over six feet six inches, properly hung against a carefully chosen background, with my brother and I ostentatiously holding the doctored tape, seemingly measured ten feet. Somewhat disappointingly however, on the same scale my brother and I appeared to be seven foot six and eight foot three respectively.

Although bitterly disappointed, we derived some consolation from having spotted this irregularity ourselves, rather than allowing the naturalist the pleasure. All other attempts at photographic faking of evidence proved equally inadequate. We had to be content with composing a carefully worded letter explaining that a pack of wild dingoes stealthily descended one night and made off with our record-making eagle's carcass, and there the matter ended.

II

I then came to the stage where I did not like killing the big birds, and the bounty price no longer tempted me. I was convinced that the eaglehawk was much maligned, and was no real menace to sheep or lambs. But I was careful to keep this opinion to myself: to do otherwise, in that district, at that time, would have been to invite tarring and feathering.

There was another reason, too. I was entranced by the beauty of the eaglehawks' soaring. For hours I used to watch them gracefully gaining height in thermals, occasionally plummeting at high speed towards the ground, and then, at the very last moment, unfolding their wings to use them as dive brakes and dramatically reduce the speed of the last few feet of the dive. Sometimes they performed these manœuvres to catch their prey, but often they appeared to wheel and swoop, and zoom up again, just from sheer *joie de vivre*. It was exhilarating merely to watch them, but I determined that when I was old enough, some way or another, I would learn to glide.

For long my ambition had been to fly. With the nonchalance of childhood I had mapped out an idyllic existence whereby I earned a living either by flying with the Royal Australian Air Force, or with Sir Charles Kingsford-Smith. In my spare time I would stooge effortlessly round the wide blue yonder in high performance sailplanes, of which there were then none in Australia.

My parents were somewhat less than enchanted with this over-simplification. They, in common with many Australians of that time, regarded aviation as a series of ill-conceived publicity stunts carried out by irresponsibles. However, while I was not actually encouraged, no barriers were put in my way.

A couple of years later I saw my first glider. Had my parents seen this extraordinary contrivance, it would merely have served to confirm their worst misgivings. It was a 1908 pattern ' hang ' glider, constructed, in secret, in an old shed by myself and two cobbers who knew no more than I. We selected this old model because the plans cost nothing, since they came from an early edition of ' The Boy Mechanic '. Materials, consisting mostly of bamboo, madapollam, piano-wire and vile-smelling glue, cost some twenty-seven shillings.

Construction took months of painstaking toil.

' The Boy Mechanic ' made the actual flying seem purely a matter of common-sense and bodily agility. We had prepared for this by constructing a primitive flight simulator, hung by ropes from the roof of the shed. We checked one another out, hanging in turn by the armpits from what, in effect, were the two upper members of the framework of a box, and swinging our legs so as to correct and control continuously changing attitudes in the rolling, yawing and pitching planes.

Eventually the aircraft was finished and ready for test flying. Although nearly frantic with anticipation, we exercised commendable self-discipline, and postponed the vital day until we had each logged an arbitrary two hours on the simulator.

We tossed for it—Arthur winning, myself as a back-up pilot, and Roy a low priority third. Arthur and I assured him that we would all share in a total of at least a dozen short flights on the first day.

We lived in the city of Bendigo, and after due research and reconnaissance, decided that the old mine dumps at the suburb of Golden Square would make an ideal test site. The dumps were artificial ' sand ' hills—the fine ' sand ' being the residue after auriferous rock had been treated by the mine batteries—and offered steep, seventy-foot faces which would be ideal for slope-soaring, if the wind was right.

D-Day came ; we were up hours before dawn, and laboriously dragged the glider, on a borrowed handcart, the two miles to the chosen dump. Secrecy was maintained during the journey, which was without mishap. Impatiently we waited for dawn, when a slight breeze, riffling the sand, gave the scene a Beau Geste touch. Green with envy, and barely concealing our impatience, Roy and I helped Arthur into the contrivance. The word ' into ' does not really mean the same as getting ' into ' an airliner: it is used in the sense that someone is helped into a suit of armour—the thing was worn rather than boarded.

Roy and I each took a wing-tip, lined up into wind, and waited for Arthur to give the word of command that would send us all hurtling towards the cliff face—Roy and I as 'erks', who would bound down the slope to await Arthur's landing—then a quick retrieve up the slope, and in turn our transformation from erks to lords of the air.

Arthur gave the word. We dashed forward. Roy and I were sure there was a net gain in height above the take-off point of about three feet as Arthur's milling legs left the ground and the machine bounded aloft. We ran down the slope—but Arthur beat us to the bottom.

I had a confused impression of the wing structure (projected by the rising sun through the madapollam) going through a quarter-flick roll to port, and flashing past us as Arthur and the machine plummeted into the sand. It did not sound like an aircraft crashing, so much as a bundle of sticks being dropped on a thickly carpeted floor—and there was Arthur, his face contorted as he struggled, up to his thighs in sand, with our once beautiful glider strewn round him like a bushfowl's nest.

He proved to be uninjured save for a badly sprained ankle, which swelled rapidly in the short time it took to dig him out and separate him from the wreckage. Without a word, Roy and I hauled him back up the slope, settled him in the handcart, then returned to estimate the damage. It was total—the longerons and wing spars were each shattered in several places. Still in silence, we hastily covered the remains with sand.

We excited some comment as we trundled Arthur home on the handcart, and hurriedly agreed that the official story for parents, teachers and those in authority was that Arthur had sprained his ankle when he fell off his bicycle.

As Roy and I left Arthur's house, we agreed that we had had a pretty raw deal. It had cost us each the best part of ten shillings, plus months of work, and Arthur had had all the fun.

That year I left school, at the tail end of the depression. Unsuccessfully I bombarded the RAAF with applications for a cadetship, and not having the money to pay for flying tuition, I went to Melbourne and, in the circumstances, was fortunate to get a job at £1 per week in an advertising agency.

By living extremely frugally, I was able to join a gliding club and work seriously at learning to fly. At least, I and everybody else in the club took it seriously; but with wise hindsight, it is difficult now to feel that it was so.

When I first joined the club, it owned a couple of primary gliders; a third had been fitted with a shoe-like nacelle and was called a secondary. This latter was regarded as a high-performance job, flown by the advanced pilots, many of whom had made slope-soaring flights of more than an hour. I was most impressed.

Apart from our hang glider, these were the first aircraft I had ever had the opportunity of touching and examining closely. All were single-seaters, and I could hardly wait until I too would fly—but in the meantime I was just happy to be able to help as ground crew, and to clean and look at them.

The CFI, the Chief Flying Instructor, was a tough character of whom I stood in great awe. He was some ten years older than I, his head looked as though it had been rough-hewn from a mallee root with an adze, and his hair was the texture of fuse-wire. He was given to laconic understatement, and preferred deeds to words.

Mostly, he treated trainees with taciturn disdain, and if any of us, for any reason at all, incurred his displeasure, he cheerfully resorted to corporal punishment—a boot where it would do most good, or a clip under the ear. This meant that I, at least, hung on his every word, gesture or expression.

He did not smoke, swear, drink or gamble, and he disapproved of anybody who did. Grudgingly he admitted that females were all right in their place, which was not a flying-field. He regarded the wearing of sun-glasses as 'sissy' and disapproved of anybody who wore a moustache.

He was a conscientious and safe pilot, but as I now realise, exceedingly hamfisted. With the training methods, this was not surprising. Since all the machines were single-seaters, methods of instruction were rudimentary. Training was undertaken at a large level field, bordered on the west by a highway and a RAAF Station, and with a second-class road running through it. The drill seemed to be to wait for a day when the wind was too strong for gliding.

The trainee was given a pretty searching oral examination by the CFI to establish the extent of his knowledge of the relevant theory of flight. If he passed, the trainee then strapped himself into one of the primaries, which was secured by a universal joint so as to hang about nine inches clear of the ground. The CFI took post at the nose of the aircraft, while other trainees held the wing-tips and tail. The aircraft was put into various attitudes and the CFI closely observed the trainee's skill and dexterity (or lack thereof) in using the controls and returning the machine to a normal gliding position. This was known as 'Wind Balancing' and after one satisfactory hour of it, the trainee was classified 'ready for ground-skids'.

251

Ground-skids required a fairly calm day. The trainee strapped himself in and the machine was fastened by a two hundred foot length of cable to an old Dodge car. He was then towed across the field, at a little less than flying speed, for about a mile. As the machine had no wheeled undercarriage, merely a central skid, the trainee was required to use aileron to keep the wings straight and level, and simultaneously steer a straight course behind the tow-car. Twelve successive satisfactory ground-skids resulted in the trainee being classified as ' ready for solo '.

The machines had a flying speed of 25 mph, so that going solo also demanded a calm day. The technique was similar to that used for ground-skids—still two hundred feet of cable, and strict instructions not to go higher than five feet. The cable could be released from both the glider and the tow-car. If a trainee proved ambitious or over-confident on first solo, the CFI would pull the release on the tow-car. This ensured the trainee's speedy return to the ground without damage to anything except his dignity—at least until the CFI got within chastising range.

I suppose nobody ever forgets his first solo. For me, although I only reached a height of a few feet, it was particularly memorable, because it was the first time I had ever flown in anything. This, I felt, made me akin to Wilbur and Orville, and the Australian J. R. Duigan, who in 1910 designed, built and flew an aeroplane, on a remote Victorian station property, without ever having seen an aircraft before.

However, I had little time to ponder on the historical aspect then, because the CFI had a longer cable hitched on, and I made several more flights at increasing heights until I reached the dizzy altitude of four hundred feet. It was my eighteenth birthday, and I was almost beside myself with joy and pride of achievement—emotions which I carefully concealed—nobody else being in any way impressed. The five or six other trainees who had solos that day doubtless felt similarly, but they also maintained poker faces.

Perhaps even the CFI was pleased, because we had not bent anything. He logged us all as ' ready for circuits ' —it was never his way to praise or congratulate ; merely to leave one in no doubt if he were displeased.

I arrived back at my lodgings flat broke—the CFI liked to collect flying fees on the spot—and felt a slight tinge of regret—from here on, life could not be anything but anticlimax.

To my landlady's queries I casually mentioned that I had been doing a little gliding. She did not hold with it —the ones with engines were dangerous enough. She was a kindly soul, however, and offered to take me to the cinema, because it was my birthday. She was puzzled when I politely declined and went off to write up my impressions in the diary which I had resolved to keep regularly.

The following weekend I was early at the field, and performed my ground-crew functions with diligence and alacrity. The CFI motioned me to strap myself in. He checked me through the pre-flight drill and stuffed a drogue parachute, attached to the end of the towing-cable, up my left trouser-leg.

" Been reading up about it?" he asked.

I nodded.

" Happy about it?"

I nodded again, not quite truthfully.

" You'll easily get a thousand feet on the launch today. Make sure you have the nose down slightly before you release. Watch the gliding angle—don't let your speed drop or you'll be in trouble. If your eyes start to water, you're flying too fast. Don't worry about a box circuit this trip. You can do a one-eighty turn as soon as you like after release, then beetle downwind and do another turn to make your approach. Don't go too far back on the downwind leg or you mightn't be able to get back into the field when you turn into wind. Make left-hand turns. Watch the attitude of the nose on the turns— aileron first and then rudder, but make it smooth. Concentrate all the time on what you're supposed to be doing. Start planning your landing as soon as you're on the downwind leg. Any questions?"

I shook my head.

Without any further ado he lifted the wing-tip and held the wings level, as a signal to the tow-car driver to take up the slack. Within a matter of seconds the machine was moving—the CFI running at the wing-tip was left behind and I was climbing away.

There was neither cockpit nor instruments. I checked the angle of attack with the horizon, and from time to time glanced between my knees to watch the tow-car belting across the red earth and brown grass.

As it neared the far limit of the field I eased the nose down and tugged at the release. The parachute pulled cleanly out of my trouser-leg as the cable fell away.

I forgot to concentrate. About four miles away, on Port Phillip Bay, a freighter painted a streak of white across the blue water. It looked beautiful. Abruptly I recalled the CFI's instructions and thought about flying.

I looked straight down on either side of my seat, to the earth twelve hundred feet below, and began my first turn in an aircraft.

Two and a half minutes after take-off I was back on the ground, having made a landing which drew no comment from the CFI. That day I made three more circuits —all I could afford.

Gradually I progressed, developing a rough empirical technique. My actual flying time was small, for the primary had a gliding angle like that of a brick, and flights seldom lasted much longer than two minutes. One compensating feature, however, was the experience gained in the comparatively large number of take-offs and landings.

Twice I landed, inwardly quaking, if not outwardly pale and trembling. Both times were on days when the CFI was absent, and his place taken by a tolerant, easy-going and rather lazy instructor.

On the first occasion I took off after forgetting to strap myself in. During the climb I flew through a down-draft, and to my horror rose slightly on the foot-wide plank which served as a seat. I nearly died of fright as I glanced down and saw the harness hanging free. I had to keep my right hand on the stick ; the left would be needed to let the cable go. Meanwhile I clutched frantically at the port flying-wire, then went through some ghastly moments nerving myself to let go this comparatively secure handhold to release the cable. The longer I delayed, the higher I climbed. The higher I climbed, the longer the flight, and all the time the earth seemed as inaccessible as the moon.

Steeling myself to make the movements smooth, I rapidly released the cable and resumed the vice-like grip on the flying-wire. There followed four of the gentlest turns ever undertaken on a primary and (much to the retrieve-crew's disgust) I landed very gently a long way up the field. This was not so much from intent as not caring where I landed. It had the added advantage of enabling me to avoid prying eyes as I vomited quietly, and used my right hand to prise the left from the flying-wire. The motor nerves seemed to be paralysed, and I could not will my hand to let go.

The retrieve-crew (consisting of my fellow trainees) knew that I had flown without fastening the harness—they had noticed it flapping about after take-off—but the instructor had not. Not that he could have been much assistance if he had noticed, but he could, quite properly, have grounded me afterwards. I shuddered to think of what the CFI might do if he found out, but he never did.

On the other occasion, my brother paid a visit to Melbourne and I took him along to see the gliding. He had never flown before. With the help of fellow trainees who diverted the instructor's attention, we both flew in the primary. I was securely strapped in, but he wedged himself into the centre-section struts, immediately behind the kingpost, to which he clung quite happily. The fueslage was nothing more than a built-up wooden girder, like one side of a bridge. The additional weight made the gliding angle quite alarming, to me, but it was a very short fast flight and pleased my brother immensely. He was not worried about the gliding angle—he thought it was always like that.

A few months after I joined the club, it took delivery of a Grunau Baby sailplane imported from Germany. Trainees were allowed to act as ground crew, and sit in it, and polish it, but that was all for the time being. The advanced pilots gradually converted on to the Grunau, and a number of trainees, who by now had made some hundreds of flights, were promoted to the secondary and slope soaring. This meant being catapulted, with a rubber shock-cord, from the top of a hill six hundred feet above the surrounding plain. The Melbourne to Sydney Highway skirted the foot of the western slope.

A difference in technique was necessary for the shock-cord launchings—the main thing being to brace the back of one's head securely against a pad, so that one's skull was not bashed in by the bulkhead at the rear of the cockpit. It was quite pleasant beating up and down the slope, and our flying time crept up for we often made flights of more than twenty minutes' duration.

One day I ventured too far north when a southerly was blowing. I had been mooning round on the far side of Sydney Road, and suddenly suspected that I was going to run out of air before I could re-cross the road to gain the approved landing area. Landing on the wrong side was frowned on by the CFI since it meant messing about manhandling the aircraft over more fences than usual, and carrying the thing across the highway.

In those days, traffic on a Sunday was comparatively light, but to offset this, the public at large was neither so tolerant nor so blasé about gliding. While they did not actually chase us with pitchforks, a number of them made it abundantly clear that this was only because they had been remiss in forgetting to bring a pitchfork. In any case it was rather embarrassing to hold up the traffic on the highway while we struggled across with an antedeluvian aeroplane ' without an engine '.

On this particular Sunday, my major error was not so much being caught too far away, as in allowing hope to triumph over reason, and thereby committing the cardinal sin of trying to stretch the glide.

Moving south-east, with the road on the port quarter, I succumbed to temptation and flew low and slow, inviting disaster, but hoping to clear the road, and an area immediately on the far side which was cluttered with small boulders hidden in the grass and impossible to land on without damage.

Eventually I could deceive myself no longer, and decided that the only chance of avoiding a prang was to land along the edge of the highway. There was no traffic ahead, and by craning my neck to peer astern, I could see that the only car was an Essex tourer, with the hood down, travelling quite a bit faster than I.

Re-assured that he would overtake me, I made a skidding turn to starboard, watching, with stunned detachment, as the wing-tip skimmed over the western roadside fence with only inches to spare. As I lined up with the road, the startled faces of the two occupants of the Essex, an elderly farmer and his wife, drifted by a few feet below.

While I landed on the grass verge at the eastern edge of the highway, the Essex continued along in front with the driver almost completely turned round in his seat, concentrating exclusively on me, as was his passenger. I was half aware that this flattering attention must inevitably lead to his running into the ditch at the side of the road, but I had troubles of my own, and after the secondary skidded to a halt, undamaged, my relief was marred by the sight of the Essex, almost on its side in the ditch.

Fortunately, the farmer and his wife were not injured, but the old gentleman lost no time in scrambling out and trotting up towards me, shaking his fist as he informed me that he was grieved to find that I was not seriously hurt. He went on to add that he might, despite his age, be able to rectify that, forthwith.

As per standing orders, I remained strapped in the nacelle. The CFI, quite rightly, was adamant about this, so as to avoid the possibility of a sudden gust capsizing the aircraft if it were left without ballast in the nose. The irate farmer was a sportsman, so he did not hit me while I remained seated. I capitalised on his chivalry, and declined to be taunted into standing up and taking my medicine like a man, being careful to assume a demeanour that would not further aggravate him by allowing him to construe my muteness as dumb insolence. I knew that the retrieve-crew with the CFI would soon turn up and I relied upon him to extricate, and eventually punish me.

About the same time as the retrieve-crew arrived so did a police motor-cycle combination. A huge rawboned sergeant unfolded himself athletically from the side-car and strolled slowly over, raising his goggles. The constable dismounted and joined him.

By this time, the farmer was dancing with rage and demanding justice—at my expense.

When the sergeant started to question me, the CFI interrupted saying that he, the CFI, was responsible. The sergeant, to my surprise, silenced the Great Man with a jerk of his thumb in the direction of the Essex, and said, " Take the mob and get that car out of the ditch. Don't come back here, or stop trying, until it's out."

Turning to the farmer, he said quietly, " I suggest you go with the constable ; he'll see they don't damage your car."

They all departed, and the sergeant said, with obvious restraint, " Supposing you tell me slowly, and truthfully, just what bloody fool caper you were up to."

As I started to comply, he interrupted me to say, "And get out of that thing and stand up when I speak to you. That's unless you're crippled in body as well as mind."

I tried to explain about the CFI, and the necessity for weight in the aircraft's nose. He made an expressive gesture, and I got out.

Apparently negligently, but with care, he threw a huge leg over the front of the nacelle to hold it secure, and said, " Don't try and old-soldier me about aeroplanes, laddie. I was in the AFC. Do you know what the AFC was?"

" The Australian Flying Corps," I replied promptly.

I thought I detected a softening of the craggy features as he continued ; " I was an Air Mechanic First Class, so I know about pilots, too. They're all mad, hare-brained bastards, and I'd have given anything to be one. I didn't have the education then, and now I'm too old. Always wanted to fly."

He paused, and emboldened, I said, " I've told you the truth, and I'm not trying to make excuses. I know what I did was stupid, but I wasn't trying to be smart. I didn't buzz the old chap."

He asked me a few routine questions and then said, " The old chap is pretty annoyed—and he has some right to be. He's after blood, but he acted stupidly too. Now you can either have this the official way, or else you can take a boot in the tail, and I'll tell him that I've dished out some rough justice. You realise I've no legal right to lay a finger on you. . . ."

As I surreptitiously massaged my backside, the sergeant said, " Go and tell that ' galah ' who says he's in charge of your mob to come over here."

I did as I was bidden, but rephrased the sergeant's words somewhat.

A few minutes later, the sergeant left the CFI with the machine and came back to the Essex, which was out of the ditch and undamaged. After a brief one-sided conversation between the sergeant and the farmer and his wife, they resumed their journey.

The sergeant then said, waving towards the secondary, " Righto. All you intrepid birdmen get back and get that thing off the road. And while I'm stationed in this District, let's have no more trouble."

He and the constable then rode away.

Reluctantly I went back to rejoin the CFI, who was examining the machine, apparently disappointed to find it undamaged. As I approached, he was rubbing his bottom. I waited for the blast, but all he ever said on the matter was, " Quite a powerful kick for a left-footer, isn't he?"

In due course I joined the ranks of the Grunau Baby pilots.

This meant a period of training at the field where we had first solo'd. There were exciting new things to learn ; aerobatics, and the first fumbling attempts at the new concept of thermal soaring. The Grunau was a single-seater, and the instruction in aerobatics paralleled our earlier efforts in solo-ing and learning to make turns.

Here I underwent another nerve-shattering experience, entirely through my own heavy-handed caution.

One day, after quizzing me on my theoretical knowledge, the CFI suggested I might care to have a bash at a couple of loops.

He stressed the need for sufficient air speed before attempting the manœuvre, and detailed all sorts of frightening consequences in default of this elementary precaution.

Nowadays it sounds surprising, but, at that stage we had had no experience of spins and the recovery therefrom, and I had no wish to stall on the top and find myself in an incipient spin, or even worse—a dreaded spiral dive. In my mind, I had a graphic picture of the earth whirling round like a top, at some crazy angle, completely out of control, while I slumped in the harness, mentally flicking through the pages of 'Flight without Formulæ' for the appropriate remedial action, and even if successful in locating it, being too terrified to put it into effective practice.

Having strapped myself in, and gone through the cockpit check, there was a cable break, and while waiting for it to be repaired, I had ample time to continue this unprofitable review of what might well be.

Examining the individual blades of grass, and all that comfortingly solid real estate stretching in all directions, I envied the small knot of non-flying onlookers who had gathered. They were waiting, with varying degrees of patience, for something to happen—preferably disastrous —and obviously to me. There was nothing personal in it : any other victim would have sufficed equally well.

In truth, of course, I did not *have* to do it. I could just unstrap myself and say I didn't want to, or I didn't feel well, or some other excuse, but I did not have the guts. I was committed, and in practice, those nearby blades of grass might as well have been six thousand feet instead of six inches beneath my seat.

The Grunau, although it had no canopy, was a far cry from the primary and secondary, even if the back of the seat was a trifle hard. Behind the pilot was the usual aperture for a back-pack parachute. Even if parachutes had been readily available in Australia, our club would not, at that stage, have considered paying all that money for such an unwarranted luxury. Instead, a piece of tastefully painted five-millimetre plywood had been neatly fitted to cover the unwanted parachute aperture and provide a backrest.

At last the cable was repaired, and take-off and launch to 1,200 feet was smooth and uneventful. Releasing the cable, I stooged for a while postponing the evil moment by unnecessarily checking varying air-speeds with their accompanying gliding angles.

I did not have much height to play with, so I lined up for the first loop, dived gently to pick up airspeed, eased the stick back, had second thoughts, and converted it into a stall—rationalising the while that this was a private check-out to make sure I would not tend to drop a wing on recovery. I repeated the performance, and then knew that it couldn't be postponed any longer.

Easing the stick well forward and then slightly increasing the dive, I hauled back on the stick, pressed hard into the seat as the ' Gs ' built up, until, just before the top, there was a terrifying crack, like a pistol shot, from behind.

I knew it—the main-spar—I'd broken it. I looked out to left and right along the wings expecting to see them fold up and meet overhead, like a carrier-borne mono-plane. Nothing happened.

The earth looked a long way down. Gingerly, and in

a state of abject petrification, I kept my index finger lightly on the stick and let the aircraft fly itself. The cliché about the moment that seems a year is true.

It was many moments before I landed—well over a mile from the normal spot for the day, and downwind. I had not dared attempt a turn, but had continued on the same heading as when coming out of the loop.

When the aircraft skidded to a stop I eased the port wing-tip on to the ground. Miraculously, the wings still did not collapse.

Of course I had merely swapped one problem for another. I had retained life at the expense of economic bondage. The Grunau had cost £750 (Australian—1937). To re-build the wings could cost at least £300. Although my salary had increased, I could envisage many years of churning out copy on perambulators, ladies' full locknit nighties, milking-machines and other equally fascinating topics, before I could repay this appalling sum. That was quite apart from the loss of revenue to the club, during the months of re-building, when the machine could not be utilised.

While I thus ruminated, the CFI rode up on his motor-cycle, his bearing and demeanour like something out of the Book of Revelation.

" Why?" he asked, with monosyllabic restraint.

He looked at me incredulously after I had explained.

" You're trying to tell me you broke or sprung the main-spar in too tight a loop, and yet you got it back on the ground, and the wing still hasn't collapsed?"

I nodded.

He unfastened inspection plates, and peered as best he could into the wing structure and the fuselage. He shook the mainplane from each tip, in turn, and then his head.

Finally he came over to the cockpit and motioned me out.

He looked up suddenly from checking the controls, and actually grinned.

" You dithering, cloth-headed clot," he said, pleasantly. " Look at the seat-back. The loop *was* too tight. Centrifugal force pressed you back into the seat, and your increased body-weight cracked the ply. *That* was the noise you heard.

" That'll cost you seven and six for a new piece of plywood, and I'll bill you for an extra flight because of the flying time lost through your landing away down here. And now, you'll take the thing up again, and do three loops good enough to please me. Just this once, if you can't afford to pay me today, you can put it on the slate until next weekend."

III

Some months later I was happily, if inexpertly, exploiting my first real thermal. The green ball of the variometer was showing a steady lift of ten feet per second. I had been in the thermal a good five minutes, and the altimeter read a comforting 3,700 feet.

Centring in the thermal had kept me so busy that I had been ' flying in the cockpit ' and not maintaining a proper lookout. There were no other aircraft flying in the area, so that this was not really dangerous—merely a tribute to my inadequacy.

Eventually I looked out to get my bearings, and was surprised to see a large eaglehawk circling diametrically opposite me.

He was watching me with polite detachment as he

soared quite effortlessly, in contrast to my concentrated wrestling with the controls. I was entranced with the languid grace and precise beauty of his every movement as he deftly maintained formation while outclimbing me. He obviously was neither afraid nor hostile, and it did not occur to me to be afraid of him.

We inspected one another, thus, for some minutes, until apparently he became bored and flapped his wings lazily a couple of times to climb high above me, so that I lost him in the sun.

When I landed, the CFI warned me of the dangers of attack from the big birds. Privately I ignored this warning as stemming from prejudiced ignorance, the CFI being country-born and bred. But I had achieved a childhood ambition, and met the eaglehawk in his own element, and almost on equal terms. Perhaps he could sense that I was one human being who understood the birds' viewpoint, and was on his side.

Over the years, there have been numerous cases of seemingly unwarranted attacks by the birds on glider pilots, until nowadays, during the summer months, some pilots only have to take off to be attacked. It almost seems as though the eaglehawks mount standing patrols, briefed to pick out these particular individuals.

On a number of occasions I have taken off in aircraft recently vacated by these unfortunates, and flown unmolested. It seemed as though the birds were shrewdly selective, and picked their marks. Perhaps, I thought, there exists a parallel to the relationship between some people and dogs. The people who are afraid, or uncertain, are credited with emitting some aura which dogs sense, and then go in to attack.

Normally, I used to keep those views to myself,

although on a couple of occasions I spoke up at Soaring Association meetings and led the opposition to motions calling for re-introduction of the bounty and widespread indiscriminate slaughter of the big birds.

All this was before last Christmas, when I embarked on a non-stop out-and-return flight, where the outward goal was an old mining town with the improbable name of Whroo.

Aided by strong thermals I had laboured mightily against brisk headwinds on the outward leg, and circling the town, photographed the control point to prove I had been there.

I set out for base, with the feeling that it was in the bag. Thermal hopping for some miles across wheatlands presented no difficulty, but over grazing country the wind changed and the thermals weakened.

I was below two thousand feet and wrestling with a not-very-promising thermal when, below, I saw a black bird soaring and flapping its wings intermittently. Soon it outclimbed me. It was an eaglehawk, but I was busy and took no particular notice..

Suddenly the eagle materialised about twenty feet above and ahead, rolled and folded its wings and dived straight at me, to pull out at what seemed inches above the canopy, and disappear behind the wing.

Thinking I had committed some breach of etiquette, possibly by pinching his thermal, I hightailed it out of the way. Apparently this was not good enough, because another eagle appeared from nowhere, in a diving head-on pass. This one pressed on in the attack configuration, with his legs lowered and his wicked-looking beak open surprisingly wide, as he squawked angrily. I could hear his squawking quite distinctly above the slipstream, as

well as that of the eagle still behind the wing. It was I
who took evasive action to avoid a collision.

The pair then took it in turns to dive-in singly—one
always coming in head-on, in a steep *kamikaze*-type attack,
while the other climbed away behind to get height for
his next attack. I tried circling tightly but one of them
was always turning inside me—not that I seriously
believed I could out-fly them. All this time I was losing
height.

Collecting my scattered wits, I did a hurried circuit
over a cleared paddock near a homestead. It was early
afternoon on a midsummer day. Most farmhouses have
telephone-wires along weathered bush poles, which tone
perfectly with the dry earth so that it is impossible to see
them from the air. The only way to locate them is by
the regular formation of their shadows. It is wise to take
one's time and plot these things carefully, prior to landing
in a strange field.

The eagles continued to harass me spasmodically, so
that although I picked out the telephone-poles, I was
forced to take evasive action rather lower than I liked,
and I finished up having to make an approach at right-
angles to what I had originally planned.

This meant some fairly coarse action with the dive
brakes and an approach underneath the telephone-wires,
and between two poles, just before touch-down.

I braked hard by digging the nose-skid into the earth,
to halt short of a fence. The friction from the steel-shod
skid set the tinder-dry grass on fire, so that I had to
forget all thoughts of standing by the nose of the aircraft
and leap out to stamp out the fire. By the time I had
done that, and dragged the aircraft up to the fence and
tied it down, the eagles were no longer in sight, and the

grazier had arrived in his Jaguar.

He was the soul of hospitality. After I had telephoned to arrange a retrieve-crew—and ignominiously confessed that I had been forced down by eagles—and helped him drink a couple of bottles of icy cold beer, he said, " Saw yuh having trouble with those bloody eagles. Lamb-killing bastards. Pity they ever abolished the bounty on 'em."

Thinking of what I must endure in the bar, back at the club, I fervently agreed.

[' Maga ' August 1964

16

SNOW ON MY TAIL
Daphne Pochin Mould

I eased back the stick so that we gained a little more height. Nearly five thousand feet now, and Carrauntual, Ireland's highest mountain, a thousand feet below us. I was entering a new world, the world of small aeroplanes flying among mountains, encountering a new experience of beauty. Below, the familiar hills of Ireland, each one of which I had climbed on foot; their ice-smoothed lower flanks and crests with splintered rocks that had stood clear of the glaciers in the Ice Age. Around Carrauntual were corrie lakes, crag-ringed, that once had nourished glaciers and sent tongues of ice down into the valley. Over there, the cleft of Ballachbeama, with its ribbon of road through the mountain line, that must have been cut by some short-lived surging torrent of Ice Age times. The sea, distant and glittering; the dark outlines of the Blasket Islands; Mount Brandon lifting from a mass of cloud. And this little plane prowling the skies close over the heights. Not mine the view of the mountaineer, the experience of the high-flying commercial pilot. I followed the road of the bird, intimate with the hills and the winds about their crests. Later, the dull reality of touch-down gave almost a feeling of shock, following this new experience of the beauty of the hills, of having encountered a new sort of reality. The same feeling came back again when in July I flew by air liner to Switzerland, and then, in small machines, under the high Alps I took the bird's road again.

Mine was a journey to a different world and yet, in a curious way, the same world. In Ireland I am almost the only person interested in flying among the hills, in Switzerland mountain flying goes on with bus-service regularity. I came from hills that bore only the marks of ice, to mountains where ice is still active, where the glacier-filled corries have become high-level aerodromes. The Trident in which I travelled swung in a great curve over the blue expanse of Lake Geneva and came in to land. My attention was divided between the Patriarch of Roumania and his suite, who had all the first-class section on board to themselves, and a row of light planes on the grass at the airport. After we had landed, a young, bearded Roumanian cleric gathered the Patriarch's considerable baggage onto a hand barrow while I waited to snatch up my rucksack.

I took the train along the shore of Lake Geneva, up into the Rhône valley and on to Sion, eating cherries that I had bought outside the station, looking at corn already harvested. At home the corn was still green. Around me were sunshine, heat, plumes of water spraying over the mountain vineyards. Then Sion, the town that looks like a picture from a book of fairy tales, yet is one of the key centres of Alpine flying.

I began by doing what every visitor does in Sion, walking through the broad streets of the new town up to the narrow alleys of the old, where the tall houses are seemingly plastered to the hillside. One comes finally to Sion's twin hills, one crowned with a castle and the other with a church. These two little rocky hills with the old buildings on their crests give Sion its unique story-book appearance. They rise suddenly from the valley floor on which the Rhône flows in great sweeping curves, and look up to the snowy heights of the high mountains. A mile along the valley, on level ground by the river, is the airfield runway.

The Swiss friend who was to take me to the airfield demonstrated with quick, mobile hands how to land on a small glacier. "You must come in low, below the level of the glacier lip, and then nose up." He used one hand held level for the ice in the corrie and the other to show the plane coming in, up valley, on a powered approach, and making a final little dip and then climb so that it should be ready to touch at the very edge of the glacier field. Always a landing uphill and a take-off downhill (shooting off the glacier lip, no matter which way the direction of the wind). We drove in his car to the airfield. On the hillsides were orchards and vineyards. "We call the Canton of Valais the California of Switzerland," he said. Sion is not a sleek, jazzed-up airport. It is strictly functional and enormously busy, with a runway that in pre-jet days was long enough to receive diverted traffic from Zurich and Geneva when they were closed by bad weather. I took it all in with an eager glance; the long tarred main runway; the Army's aircraft and buildings on the far side; the sun-scorched grass on which small aircraft normally land; the park with its line of brightly-coloured light aeroplanes; the hangars, offices, and the restaurant where people were sitting on a tiny terrace drinking coffee.

All the time, aircraft were on the move. Piper Cubs belonging to the Aero Club doing 'circuits and bumps'. Gliders circling higher and higher overhead, while one little plane did a regular routine of tow-outs to a considerable height above the valley, and then came racing back to pick up the next sailplane, side-slipping off his height to get down quickly. Three helicopters, one a mighty French-built Alouette III, jet-engined, belonging to Air-Rescue and able to carry a couple of stretcher cases. Inside Air Glacier's hangar I noticed the names of high-level mountain huts posted on the walls, and in front of each the pile of goods awaiting transport to it— bottled gas, packaged soups, rucksacks, boxes of every kind, building materials, assortments as varied as the cargoes of coasting steamers.

In the evening I saw Hermann Geiger on the grass runway, waving with corrective gestures to a solo student who was bouncing his landings. Geiger was born in the Sion hills, of a poor family, in 1914. Apprenticed to a garage, he saved petrol-pump tips and used them to join the Sion Glider Club when it was formed. More saving allowed him to take a half-hour lesson on a power-plane. Ultimately he won through, bought his own Piper Cub, and fitted it with a sling which he used for dropping supplies in the mountains, including hay to starving sheep and chamois. Taking food to the wild deer in winter is now part of Sion's ordinary flying. Geiger was a short, stocky, dark-haired Swiss, shy and liable to vanish when you wanted to talk to him about his exploits. In the early 1950s he had been a pioneer of glacier landings, constantly engaged in rescue work. I cornered him one day, and learned that he had flown 3,552 rescue flights, and that he had 340 hours logged in gliders, 2,600 in helicopters, and 9,000 in fixed-wing engined aircraft. "Did you ever have engine failure?" I asked. "Yes, twice, up by the Matterhorn. And then I did as the *chouca* (mountain raven) and the eagle do, and glided back to this airfield."

The Aero Club's planes came home to roost. The gliders were shrouded in dustsheets and slung from the hangar roof, and the power-driven aircraft were parked below. I was impatient to get airborne. I gazed at the mountain sides leaping up from the level floor of the Rhône valley, grassy and wooded on their lower slopes, their peaks bare and snowy above. Bruno Bagnoud, tall, quiet, ex-mountain guide and ski instructor, now director of the air company, told me to telephone him early next morning.

Flying begins with first light, when the air is calm, before the big thermal upcurrents that the gliders soar on build up. After a quick breakfast I called the airfield. "We are loading timber for Tracuit," said Bruno. "Come at once." Ordering and waiting for a taxi would have wasted time. I trotted down the road beside the railway line to the airfield. Piles of neatly sawn pine logs were being packed into a Pilatus Porter, and some small boys were climbing in and out, already imagining themselves pilots taking the eagle's road among the peaks. This is a large plane driven by a powerful turbo-jet engine and a propeller; the Swiss designed it for such work. It can carry eight or nine people, and lifts parties of skiers, climbers and sightseers regularly. With the seats removed, it takes an equivalent weight in goods. It has a rugged fixed undercarriage and tail wheel, and steel skis are fitted to all three wheels.

I climbed in over the timber, and sat beside Bruno

Bagnoud. A second man couched himself on the wood, a lifeline attached to his belt. Bruno started up, did a rapid check, called the tower by radio, and swung round on the brown grass for take-off. He opened up to full throttle and we lifted off. It was a real STOL machine, designed for short take off and landing. It has to be for the places where it flies. " She's heavy," he told me above the engine's noise. " You always feel a weight in your hands when flying her."

Sion lies just north of the wall of the Alps. Bruno was proud to tell me that seventy per cent of all rescue flights went out from its airfield. All the high places, and high huts, are only a brief flying time away. Tracuit hut is on the Alpine backbone, north-west of the Weisshorn.

It was a mundane job of work, taking firewood up to the hut. But for me this was a first experience of Alpine flying, and also my first encounter with the Alps at close quarters. We did a climbing turn out from Sion, with the old town and its twin hills below, and the new town spilling out round them, and climbed away over the foothills, the green alpine grass, the pines, the brown wooden chalets, and the mountain villages with the roads snaking up to them in sequences of hairpin bends. All round was the great line of the Alps, the peaks whose very names thrill anyone with a feeling for mountains. We gazed on rock and snowfield, on glaciers in the corries, on glaciers winding down the valleys, crevassed and dirtied with the long stony trails of moraines. Fluffy cumulus cloud lay on some crests, and in fleecy strips on the flanks.

This was a different sort of flying from whisking an Auster over Irish hills with a thousand feet of clearance in hand. The laden Pilatus was inching herself up, and was only just going to slip over a col ahead. We were flying very close to the ground on the side of the hill. I could look down and see the stones and aline plants below us, and at the rocky ridge ahead. But I had confidence in the machine and its mountaineer-pilot.

We passed over a high-level reservoir and hydro-electric dam, the Lac de Moiry, its water tinged with glacier water that is always milky with comminuted rock and dirt. Carrying supplies to such construction projects is part of the work of Alpine pilots. This very week Bruno was waiting for a parcel of fish stock to drop by helicopter into one of the mountain lakes.

We were flying at a great mountain wall, sheeted with glittering snow and ice. On the one hand lay a drop to the valley, on the other a steep icefield. The Tracuit hut, sturdily built, stood in the rocks where they out-cropped on the edge of the ridge. Bruno circled, and faced the dazzling white of the snowfields. I found myself losing horizon and direction as the plane swung close in to the ice. The crewman was piling the logs over the trap door in the plane's floor. We turned again, and saw men from the hut standing at their doorway. We made a straight, low run in towards them. At the critical moment the release was pulled, the trap door opened and logs scattered down close to the hut. Bruno did a second run to drop the rest of our cargo. Then the lightened plane soared away and hastened back to Sion.

Another Pilatus was loaded, this time for a ski landing, and I went with Bruno in her. We had a big load of food and other stores, and headed for the Bertol hut, which lies between Mont Collon and the Tête Blanche. We were not long off Sion strip when Bruno put the selector over from wheels to skis and racked them down. The weather was not good. There was cloud on the heights ahead of us, and below the snow and ice looked dull and sinister. This sort of flying demands a pilot who is a mountaineer and who knows, and maybe loves, the hills. Then he will be sensitive to the winds channelled and twisted by peak and col and valley, to the look of the snow, packed or powdered, wet or dry, and to the signs that herald the sudden and violent storms of the high places. We got clear of the cloud and flew under blue skies, over white snow through which rocky peaks jutted darkly. Bruno pointed to snow pluming from the cornices. The windsock had hung limp at Sion, but up here the wind was strong. He waved a casual hand toward a slender, rocky height level with us. "Cervin," he said. "The Matterhorn."

The brown timber walls of the Bertol hut stand on a rocky ridge, below a small glacier snowfield. A glacier landing is not easy. It must be exactly right. You must land once you have committed yourself to doing so. You cannot, as on an ordinary airfield, open up and 'go round again', for an attempted overshoot would run you straight into the crags at the back of the corrie. You need to land precisely, to get all the benefit of what run there is and to use to the full the uphill slope and so avoid problems of stopping and turning. Bruno made his final checks. The skis were in position and locked down. We faced into the white expanse. It is tricky, judging your exact distance off the ground on unbroken snow. But the skis touched neatly and we were bumping across the hard snow. Snow, like water, is a lot harder than it looks. The Pilatus can use reverse thrust to brake, and we swung round to face downhill, ready for take-off, with the propeller running fast in reverse pitch to hold her securely.

We flung open the doors and jumped out. From the valley heat to this—air, crisp and clear, an exhilaration to breathe. Sunshine from a blue sky. Sparkling, untrodden snow around us, and ringing crags and peaks. Two men from the hut came to greet us, and to help unload the packages onto the snow. The work was done expertly and swiftly. Doors open, out with the goods, a handshake and a word of farewell. Then we were off and away, over the glacier lip into the valley below. Swinging round and back, we flew low over the snowfield, through the col close to the hut on the rocks, and set course for home.

Even in this short time the weather had changed. The Alps rose from a cloud sea that had formed, a thin cover that shrouded most of what was below us. It was evident that Bruno recognised each of those jutting pinnacles of snow-streaked rock as an old friend, perhaps with memories of climbs he had made on them, of parties he had led. Thus he could confidently put down the nose of the aeroplane into the cloud between these familiar landmarks, and come safely into the valley, heading back for Sion, with the long nose of the Pilatus slanting steeply ahead of us and the Rhône valley far below. Bruno called on the radio and Sion tower answered, giving us clearance to go straight in and land. He checked that the wheels this time, and not the skis, were on position. We flared out over the end of the field, lost height, and sank onto the sun-burnt grass,

He swung the plane round by the hangars, and stopped the engine. We stepped out. The tail ski was still packed with hard snow from the glaciers ; it was dribbling in the valley sun. Bruno picked out a little to make a ball and cool off his hands. I had been reading the warnings about flying high, making quick ascents and descents like this without oxygen. Above ten thousand feet you must use oxygen, the books said. So I asked: " Do you feel the height, the sudden changes?" "No, not at all," he replied. " Unless one has a cold, when one might get a bit of headache." Bruno was well used to the heights from childhood. My own experience was less, of the four thousand feet of the Cairngorms, rather higher in Iceland. But I found the quick ascents to the Alpine huts around the ten thousand foot level without any physical effects, and their reward was the sheer delight of coming up to the high places of rock and snow and blue sky.

The next morning, very early, I dialled the airfield number again. M. Bagnoud was flying, but was expected to be down by eight o'clock. I arranged to go with him on the last flight of the morning to the Rothorn hut. Our load was a heavy one of angle irons for a constructional job, topped off by a large cardboard box of freshly-baked loaves.

" The same direction as yesterday, only more beautiful," was how Bruno Bagnoud described the way we were to go. The hut, he explained, was on the Zermatt side of the Zinalrothorn; we must climb over near to that mountain, and between the Dent Blanche and the Weisshorn ; the Matterhorn would be right before us. The start of the flight did not suggest we would see very much, since the whole valley was hazy with heat. But once we had gained a few thousand feet, we left the haze below and came out into a world of sparkling light, of snow and rock and glacier, and of clear skies with small, fleecy, fine-weather cumulus clouds forming here and there among the heights. We looked down, steeply and deeply, into a narrow Alpine valley of green grass and patches of darker forest, with a road winding up to a hillside village. Above, the mountains of black rock and white snowfields towered over the pastures and trees.

We clawed our way upward among the heights of frost-splintered rock and gleaming snow and ice, a red plane loaded with angle irons and the morning's bread making her way past a great sweep of snow-covered glacier, steeply sloping, with the feathered snow plumes of a recent snow avalanche thrown across its surface. We looked at a textbook example of a valley glacier, winding its way down, its surface regularly streaked with moraines —stones and rock powder torn from the mountain flanks by the passage of the ice. We flew on and over, and finally saw the solid, grey, stone-built hut on a spur of rock jutting out into a snowfield. It was hard to see, until Bruno pointed it out. Nobody met us. We landed on the lonely white expanse, tossed out our load beside the pile left by the previous flights of the morning, and took off again.

The Rothorn landing place was beautiful almost beyond belief ; a flashing little plain of white snow and ice, looking out to encircling hills, with the Matterhorn leaping up amongst them. On one side was a drop to the valley. This was the way we took off, shooting off the corrie lip. Behind us were great crags cradling a little glacier which came down in a white and gleaming icefall to the landing place.

If you go up early enough and high enough, you can ski throughout the summer in Switzerland, and fixed-wing aircraft and helicopters take people up to do so. As we headed for Sion we passed over a snowy plain where people were skiing, and Bruno went low over them in greeting, and they looked up and waved to us. At

Sion, we talked about the Matterhorn. A conference of Alpine guides was taking place, and parties were to climb the mountain from several sides and meet on the summit. Among us was an American photographer, an ex-wing-walker, who said he was one of the few to fall off a plane without a parachute and survive. He had saved himself by snatching hold of a strut. He was discussing with Bruno Bagnoud certain possibilities. Could he photograph the climbing guides, or be let down from a helicopter onto the summit? I left Sion while the matter was still being considered. The American had to be disappointed. But evidently a seed had been sown in M. Bagnoud's mind, to germinate a few weeks later. At the end of July 1966 he was flying home in a helicopter after a rescue operation. It was 5.30 a.m., calm, with a steady wind. There was Cervin, the Matterhorn. He made an approach. Was it possible? He thought so, and came in again, and touched down on the very summit, a tiny plateau. He stayed there long enough, his rotors still turning, to be certain that in case of need, and with conditions favourable, a helicopter could land there and leave rescuers to aid those in trouble high on the mountain.

As for me, I went on exploring Switzerland, marvelling at the rich variety of scenery in this tiny country only half the size of Ireland. I sat on the heights of the Diablerets glacier, with Valais on the one hand and the green, wooded valleys and timber-built villages, gay with window-boxes, of the Bernese Oberland on the other, and watched a glacier training flight in progress. The Diablerets glacier is really a great undulating ice-cap, with plenty of space, and nothing ahead to hit if you misjudge and overshoot. I saw a small blue-green trainer, iridescent like a dragonfly, come up the valley from the Montreux direction, and turn in past the terminal of the cable way, and set about circuits and landings, at ten thousand feet, a tiny dark speck moving over glittering white.

Neuchâtel, in the more open and pastoral country, backed by the gentler heights of the Jura, has a big maintenance firm beside its airfield. The plant is as clean and scientific as a laboratory, with banks of instrumentation to check engines and instruments. Neuchâtel is the centre of the Swiss watchmaking industry, and they told me it was the skilled men from that trade who graduated into work on aircraft instruments. Across the way, beside the field, is a riding-school. I moved from the new to the old, from the aircraft shop to stable smells, to horses' heads leaning out from looseboxes to nibble one's shoulder, and I rode through the woods on a retired French racehorse.

Ultimately I came to Zurich and to the headquarters of Air Rescue, and met Fritz Buhler. He is one of those rare people who are incredibly busy and yet who give the impression they have all the time in the world to talk to you personally. I caught him in the evening, at his big office in the new block by the lakeside. Once again I met the mountainy background. Fritz has long experience as a pilot. He is also a climber and has run a ski-school. We talked about Alpine flying. It has developed only since the last war. The American Piper Cub played, and still plays, an important part in it ; the Pilatus aeroplane is very much like a larger and more powerful Cub. Freddy Wissel, the St Moritz hotelier-pilot, made the first ski landing in 1951, and it was regarded as very risky. Hermann Geiger made his first one in a Cub, on one of the wide open spaces of high-level snow and ice, in 1952. He left an amusing account of how he gingerly touched down, his head full of stories of overturning and disaster prophesied by his friends. He found himself skiing along safely and smoothly. He took off again, and soon was doing circuits and landings on the snowfield. How easy it was, how wasted the years when he might have been doing it! Alas, across my brief summer meetings with Geiger, and with his wife and family in their new Sion home, there lies the shadow of tragedy. Six weeks later Geiger was killed when the aircraft in which he was taking off to give a flying lesson collided with a glider.

Progress has been such that today the Swiss Alpine Club limits the number of places where climbers and skiers may be landed from the air. Otherwise the soli-tudes of the mountains would be shattered by flying machines landing, like flies on honey, all over them. Rescue work grew up in a similar way. At first, doctors and medical supplies were dropped by parachute. Ski landings changed the whole picture. Missed targets and lost goods became things of the past. Precision take-offs and landings mean that today sick mountain farmers and injured skiers can be whisked away to hospital in a matter of minutes.

In 1960 Fritz Buhler set about creating Air Rescue in its present form. It is a voluntary organisation, financed by gifts, some contributions from Swiss Cantons, and by those who have been rescued and who can afford to pay something. He told me how the service is run. Nine airfields in Switzerland are used. " My hobby is the weather in the mountains. Meteorology isn't yet an exact science, so there is still room for an amateur like me. I've made a special study of snow, how it varies from wet-packed slush to powder. Wet snow contains hardly any air; an avalanche will suffocate those it engulfs immediately. But a fall of powdery snow contains lots of air, and people can survive in it till dug out. A pilot must learn to judge snow conditions by looking down, using the glitter or lack of it to show what sort of surface he will have to land on. Switzerland is a most difficult country meteorologically."

He turned to the big-scale map on the office wall to point out the four regions into which the state is divided for rescue purposes—four divisions based on weather. He called his secretary, who began to hand me papers. Red, multilingual posters, giving basic instructions on how to call Rescue, how to mark a landing place, how to signal to the rescue plane or helicopter. " That's indestructible paper," he explained. " You can crumple it, wet it, and still read it." The posters are in all sizes, and are put up wherever they may be of use. To get a rescue going, one telephones Zurich Control Tower. " They're always on duty, and know where I am, or whoever is in charge for me." Fritz or his deputy then telephones back. He gave me another paper, listing in French and German the essential questions to ask the caller—what has happened, where, the nature of the accident or illness, the help available (should the pilot bring extra help, or not?), and the state of the weather. Fritz's office then selects an airfield with the necessary equipment and asks them to tackle the job. " With a plane," he added, " you needn't fly the patient to the nearest hospital. In a few minutes you can take him to the hospital best suited to deal with the emergency." He showed me a 1965 Report listing 220 rescues effected, involving 1,081 flights.

Fritz was flying to South America that night. " I haven't packed yet," he said. After I left him, and before making his own departure, he received an emergency call, and organised yet another rescue operation.

I returned to Geneva. As my Trident took off for England, I looked out at Mont Blanc, remote and white and glittering in the sun. But not really remote any more, when I thought of the intimacy with the mountains of Alpine flying, of the close and profound experience of the beauty of rock and glacier and high forest and pasture, and of the Pilatus touching down on the burned, brown grass of Sion, with her tail ski packed with hard frozen glacier snow.

[' Maga ' March 1967

BIOGRAPHICAL NOTES
ON THE AUTHORS

A CHAPTER OF ACCIDENTS   Air Vice-Marshal T. C. Traill,
C.B., O.B.E., D.F.C.

Born in the Argentine. Educated R.N. College Osborne (1912)
and Cambridge (M.A., 1924). 1914-1918: midshipman in
H.M.S. *Nelson* at the Dardanelles. Became a Royal Flying
Corps pilot and commanded a flight of Bristol Fighters on the
Western Front. 1919-1938: Assistant Air Attaché, Washington,
and served in Iraq, Transjordan and Egypt. 1939-1945: commanded a bomber station and served on staffs in Bomber
Command and the Air Ministry, and in North Africa. Post-
war, Air Officer Commanding groups in Germany and Fighter
and Coastal Commands. Became Director-General of Personnel,
Air Ministry. Retired 1954.

DIFFERENT TECHNIQUES *and*
THE BREATH OF LIFE   (Pen name) ' A. G. D. '

Air Vice-Marshal A. G. DUDGEON, C.B.E., D.F.C. Born in Egpyt ;
there learned to speak Arabic of the colloquial kind. Educated
Eton and R.A.F. College Cranwell. Served in India for five
years. Early in the war, posted to the Middle East, where he
flew a hundred operational sorties. Returned to the United
Kingdom to command a large Dakota-Horsa glider station for
D Day. Later, in a Jeep, carrying a radio set and revolver,
became involved with the Germans outside Arnhem. After the
war, commanded fighter wings in Singapore and Germany and
a transport wing in the U.K., and served in staff appointments.
Now on the Defence Staff at the British Embassy in Washington. Logbook lists over a hundred different types of aircraft
flown, including gliders, sailplanes, an airship and a free
balloon. Ambition: to add to it a man-lifting kite.

SUN TAN 27   (Pen name) 'Nosmo'

Air Vice-Marshal H. H. BROOKES, C.B., C.B.E., D.F.C. Educated
Bedford School and R.A.F. College Cranwell. Test pilot for
four years at Martlesham Heath; bomber squadrons in the
United Kingdom and Iraq. World War II, Bomber Command
and overseas. In all served nine years in Iraq, and was the
last Air Officer Commanding the R.A.F. in that country. On
retiring from the Service, became personnel manager of a large
mining group in Rhodesia.

SUNDAY DAWN, SUNDAY DUSK *and*
THE LONG WAY BACK   D. E. Charlwood

Born in Melbourne. In the depression of the 30s, worked on
a grazing property in the far west of Victoria that later became
the setting for many of his stories. Served as a R.A.A.F. navigator with Bomber Command in World War II, and his first
book, *No Moon Tonight,* conveys the mood and atmosphere of
squadron life as the ordinary aircrew knew it. After the war
joined the Directorate of Civil Aviation in Melbourne, and is
responsible for selecting and training air-traffic controllers. In
1965 wrote *All the Green Year,* a novel of boyhood in Australia
which is now set for study in many schools there. In 1966 a
collection of his stories was published under the title of AN
AFTERNOON OF TIME.

TOTEM FLIGHT 347   (Pen name) 'Jonathan Spence'

J. S. DUNKLEY joined the R.A.F. in 1941 and trained as a pilot
in Texas under the U.S. aid-scheme. He then served with a
Close-Support squadron (parachute-dropping) in Burma. In
1946 he became a civil airline pilot on African, Eastern and
South American routes. Since 1957 he has been mostly on the
North American and Carribean route. Now flying the 'big
jets'. Total flying time, about fourteen thousand hours.

A GLIMPSE OF THE STRATOSPHERE   Tony Smythe

Son of Frank Smythe, the mountaineer. Educated Wycliffe
College. Eight years in the R.A.F. as a pilot in Canberra

bomber and night ground-attack squadrons and a Javelin all-weather fighter squadron. Became a climbing instructor in Snowdonia. With a friend in 1962 did a two-man expedition to Canada and Alaska, hunting with the Indians, working in a silver mine, and ascending two unclimbed peaks in the McKinley Range. In 1964 explored Eastern Europe and Russia with his wife. In 1966 they spent six months climbing and sight-seeing in Peru, Bolivia and Chile. Lectures, writes and broadcasts about climbing and travel.

How Goes It ?   (Pen name) 'M. D. L.'

Air Vice-Marshal M. L. LYNE, A.F.C. (two bars). Educated Imperial Service College and R.A.F. College Cranwell. Spitfire pilot ; shot down covering the Dunkirk evacuation. Returned to active service in 1941, joining the Merchant Ship Fighter Unit—Hurricanes catapulted from the decks of merchant ships (usually having to land on the sea afterwards). Escorted eight convoys. Later commanded a jet fighter squadron, and in 1947 led the first team to perform aerobatics in jet aircraft at an international air display. As a member of the R.A.F. Flying College staff, did several research flights in polar regions. Air Attaché Moscow, 1961. Commandant R.A.F. College Cranwell, 1963. Now Air Officer Commanding 23 Group, training pilots entering direct from civil life.

Skydiving   John Allen

Educated Wellington College, Sir George Williams University Montreal (B.A.) and Brigham Young University Utah (M.A.). Has travelled in Egypt, Morocco, North America, Mexico and Cuba, and taught in Switzerland and Canada. Other activities —fighting forest fires, snow and salt-water skiing, gliding. Now working for Ph.D. in XVIth century diplomatic history.

The Cumulo-Nimbus Cloud   (Pen name) 'James Thomson'

Squadron Leader J. GLADSTONE entered the R.A.F. as an aircraft apprentice in 1938. Served in the Middle East, 1941-1945. Commissioned as a pilot in 1951. Has flown mainly in Transport and Coastal Command squadrons. Awarded the Air Force Cross in 1957 and a bar to the Cross in 1964.

BIOGRAPHICAL NOTES

'LEADS THE FIELD'   Wing Commander K. P. Smales,
                                                    D.S.O., D.F.C.

Educated Norbury College. Commissioned in the R.A.F. in
1937. World War II, served with the Advanced Air Striking
Force in France, and in Hampden and Lancaster squadrons.
1942, took part in the thousand-bomber raid on Cologne; 1943,
wounded on a Berlin raid, and spent four months in hospital.
Afterwards served in staff appointments and commanded
squadrons and wings of Canberras and Javelins. Now a Group
Captain, Air Attaché at Buenos Aires.

THE AIR RACE   Brian Haimes

Has been fascinated by aeroplanes since the age of twelve.
Barred by short sight from becoming a fighter pilot in 1940,
joined the Indian Army. Did parachute and glider work with
the XIVth Army and several R.A.F. and U.S.A.F. transport
squadrons. In 1948 entered the University of Western Australia
to become an aeronautical engineer; some years later graduated
from the University of Oxford as an economist. Found that
the oil companies paid the best salaries, so then spent eleven
happy years roaming the world as a member of the Shell
Petroleum Company's Aviation Department.

RE-BORNE WITH WINGS   John Brooks

Left Cambridge in 1939 to enroll as a trooper in the Royal
Tank Regiment. Commissioned into the Yeomanry, and later
transferred to the R.A.F. Volunteer Reserve. Returned to
Cambridge to resume reading science, and graduated M.A.
Rejoined the R.A.F. at the time of the Korean war. Became a
flying instructor, and concluded happily by joining the staff of
the Cambridge University Air Squadron. Has written prose
and verse for several 'glossy' magazines, and is now a full-time
author.

AQUILINE ACTIVITY   James Montgomery Robinson

Educated Bendigo High School and Diplomatic Australian
School of Pacific Administration. Advertising copywriter,

radio-script author, rubber worker, lorry driver, jackaroo, native affairs officer (Papua and New Guinea). Operational war service in the South-West Pacific ; now Royal Australian Air Force active reserve. Has been gliding sporadically since 1937, and has dabbled in power flying, ballooning, parachuting and flying gyrocopters.

SNOW ON MY TAIL   Daphne Pochin Mould

Graduated B.Sc. (geology, 1st class honours) at Edinburgh University in 1945, and Ph.D. in 1946. Has written fifteen books about Scotland and its Islands, and Ireland, and their Celtic Saints. Has also visited and written about Iceland, Greenland, the Faroes, Switzerland, France, Italy and Greece. Learned to fly at Cork in the early 1960s. Is keen on small boats, mountain-walking and photography. Now lives in Ireland.